GENDER, SCIENCE,
& the
UNDERGRADUATE
CURRICULUM

BUILDING TWO-WAY STREETS

EDITED BY Caryn McTighe Musil

D1303605

Any opinions, findings, and conclusions or recommendations expressed in this material are those of the author(s) and do not necessarily reflect the views of the National Science Foundation.

 ASSOCIATION OF AMERICAN COLLEGES AND UNIVERSITIES

This material is based upon work supported by the National Science
Foundation under Grant No. (HRD 9555808).

*To order additional copies of this publication or to find out about other AAC&U publications, e-mail
pub_desk@aacu.nw.dc.us or call 202/387-3760.*

table of contents

It is both an honor and deeply gratifying to find my own essay, "Building Two-Way Streets: The Case for Feminism and Science," which argues for the mutual importance of feminism to science (and vice versa), referred to so often in *Gender, Science, and the Undergraduate Curriculum*. Nothing can be more satisfying to an academic than to know that her work has influenced others to break old molds and build new ones. But it is not for vanity that I urge people to read this book. *Gender, Science, and the Undergraduate Curriculum* represents the very best of academia. Its essays show knowledge in the process of formation. The various authors are not afraid for us to watch as they struggle with the uncertainty of new ideas and new pedagogies. And it is the willingness to struggle, to accept and work with uncertainty that is—or at least ought to be—the hallmark of academic life. Because we are unsure, we search for new knowledge, and the search stimulates us and strengthens our students as they, too, learn not predigested facts, but how to search.

I applaud the National Science Foundation and its Program on Women and Girls for funding the Association of American Colleges and Universities' three-year grant, *Women and Scientific Literacy: Building Two-Way Streets*. NSF's acknowledgment of the value of such investigative work in new areas of scholarship and teaching should encourage more institutions and more faculty members to explore additional ways to engage students in scientific questions.

Traditionally, when scientists speak of scientific literacy, they have a list of concepts that they wish members of an informed public to understand—evolution, gravity, atomic theory, Euclidean geometry, etc. But as Caryn McTighe Musil writes, the project described in this book "suggests that to be scientifically literate is to be able to ask intelligent questions about scientific claims." To do this, one needs to be able not only to question particular observations or experiments, but also to examine their social context. How and why were particular questions formulated? How and why did scientists choose the particular experimental or observational approaches aimed at answering them? Whose interests were served and whose ignored? How were the results interpreted and how were the interpretations applied? These are the types of questions that two generations of feminist science studies scholars have been asking and answering.

In the essays in this book interdisciplinary groups of scholars and teachers struggle with how to integrate the feminist science studies scholarship into the teaching of basic science and how to insert more basic science into the teaching of women's studies. Each discipline or sub-discipline presents particular difficulties and opportunities to be coped with. It is the virtue of this book that writings address courses that range from biology and health (always the easy cases for gender integration projects) to chemistry and mathematics. This book is a beginning, and I hope it will inspire new teaching experiments and new ways of thinking about science itself. There is still much to do, but, happily, we have also moved a fair way along the road.

ANNE FAUSTO-STERLING
Professor of Biology and Women's Studies, *Brown University*

This book could not have been written had the science and women's studies faculty at ten colleges and universities not opted to invest in a cross disciplinary study of the provocative and fascinating field of feminist science studies. They did so in the belief that science could be taught better, conceived of more broadly, and made accessible even to students who might have avoided it most of their lives. To the administrators who supported them, the team leaders who provided organizational continuity throughout the life of the project, and the many faculty who participated in a wide range of forums, lectures, seminars, and workshops, I extend my gratitude. The full list of participants is listed in Appendix A, but I want to acknowledge the following institutions for the national leadership they have provided for others: University of Arizona, Barnard College, Bates College, California State University - Long Beach, Greenfield Community College, University of Illinois at Chicago, Portland State University, University of Rhode Island, Rowan University, and Saint Lawrence University.

The project would not have been possible had the National Science Foundation, and in particular, its Program on Women and Girls, not recognized that it was necessary not simply to recruit girls and women into science but to expand the understanding of science itself in light of the scholarship on women and gender which has been produced over the last three decades. For her expansive vision as I was writing the original proposal, *Women and Scientific Literacy: Building Two-Way Streets,* I want to acknowledge in particular Dr. Sue V. Rosser, who then was the director of the program on women and girls at NSF. NSF is responsible for spurring much of the science education reform in the nation. It understands that our country needs scientifically literate citizens if we are to be socially responsible and capable of dreaming new worlds into existence, even as we come to understand more fully the one we already live in.

Although I was listed as the official project director, I really shared those duties, both the conceptualization and the implementation, with my longtime colleague and friend, Dr. Debra Humphreys. It was she who would have edited this volume to its conclusion had she not been tapped last December to be AAC&U's new vice president for communications and public affairs. Her bold intellect, formidable organizational skills, and sheer joy in plunging into new areas of investigation left their mark on the project, on this final book, and certainly on my life.

Both Debra and I have our doctorates in English. We therefore knew better than to presume we could lead a science project on our own. I want to acknowledge how much the project's success was enhanced because of the distinguished and dedicated leadership from the National Advisory Board of Science Scholars: Dr. Margaret Palmer of the University of Maryland; Dr. Karen Barad formerly of Pomona College and now of Mount Holyoke College; Dr. Angela B. Ginorio of the University of Washington; Dr. Evelynn Hammonds of Massachusetts Institute of Technology; Dr. Cathy Middlecamp of the University of Wisconsin-Madison; Dr. Bonnie Spanier of the University at Albany-SUNY; and Dr. Joan Polinar Shapiro of Temple University. Their accumulated knowledge was staggering, their intellectual exploration of feminist science studies' challenging questions was riveting, and their commitment to increasing students' engagement in science was an inspiration.

The Association of American Colleges and Universities has been blessed with a remarkably talented staff. The NSF project and this resulting publication have benefited from that reservoir of talent. Special thanks go to two program associates, Lee Harper and Brinton Ramsey, who worked on the project in its first two phases, and to a third program and research associate, Daniel Teraguchi, who was responsible for gathering the essays and handling the preparation for publication of this final volume. He was assisted in the manuscript preparation by AAC&U program associate Michelle Cooper, and she in turn was assisted by our summer intern, Elena Khatskevich.

I also want to thank Dr. Bridget Puzon, senior editor, at AAC&U for her quickness and deftness in editing the collection of essays and Julie Warren for ensuring that the design and publication process pleased everyone. Suzanne Hyers weighed in to coordinate the overall schedule for the production and marketing of the final publication.

It has been a gift to direct *Women and Scientific Literacy* and edit its final publication, *Gender, Science, and the Undergraduate Curriculum.* To the feminist science scholars, the National Advisory Board, and the faculty participating in the project, I offer my deepest gratitude. Collectively you helped me recover my love of science and gave me the courage to explore the endless questions it provokes. What you did for me, you do every day for multitudes of students. On their behalf, we all thank you.

CARYN MCTIGHE MUSIL
July 14, 2001

Hermit Crabs, Women, and Scientific Literacy

Caryn McTighe Musil

In *High Tide in Tucson* (1995), Barbara Kingsolver tells the story of how a hermit crab, resting innocently in a shell on the shore in the Bahamas, inadvertently ended up on a coffee table in Tucson, Arizona. As she was walking along a Caribbean beach, Kingsolver had collected several shells to bring back to her daughter. One of them happened to be Buster the Crab's mobile home. It wasn't until Kingsolver's daughter was counting and sorting the shell collection that "the largest, knottiest whelk had begun to move around," extending "one long red talon of a leg, tap-tap-tapping like a blind man's cane." Unbalanced by the momentous dislocation, "with red stiletto legs splayed in all directions, it lunged and jerked its huge shell this way and that." As mother and daughter "watched in stunned reverence, the strange beast found its bearings and began to reveal a determined crabby grace. It felt its way to the edge of the table and eased itself over, not falling. . .but hanging suspended underneath within the long grasp of its ice-tong legs, lifting any two or three at a time while many others still held in place. In this remarkable fashion it scrambled around the underside of the table's rim, swift and sure and fearless like a rock climber's dream."

In the Association of American Colleges and Universities' (AAC&U) curriculum and faculty development project, *Women and Scientific Literacy: Building Two-Way Streets,* the scientists and non-scientists alike came to identify strongly with Buster the Crab. Each felt as if he or she had been whisked off to unfamiliar territory where adaptation depended on one's ability to use both skills already mastered as well as those not yet cultivated. Many times one could hear the tap-tap-tapping of the metaphoric cane as people felt their way and eased over the edge of the known to dangle somewhat precariously over the precipice. During the course of the project, however, most participants from many different disciplines managed, as Buster had done, to find their bearings. Eventually they, too, moved with "a determined crabby grace" into the world—not of the arid desert—but of feminist science studies.

Since 1996, AAC&U has been working with cross-disciplinary faculty teams at ten colleges and universities through a National Science Foundation (NSF) grant to deepen the knowledge about feminist science studies and to generate new, or modify existing, undergraduate courses where this scholarship is taught (The full list of schools and participating faculty members can be found in Appendix A). The project assumes that feminist science studies is a vehicle for creating new intellectual pathways among the sciences, social sciences, and humanities. The impetus for the project came most directly from Dr. Anne Fausto-Sterling, a distinguished biologist at Brown University. In her article, "Building Two-Way Streets: The Case of Feminism and Science" (1992, 336-349), she poses the troubling question, "How do we reproduce a world in which science seems an illegitimate place for women and gender studies seems an inappropriate enterprise for scientists?" She argues that science needs feminism and feminism needs science. Until there are far more communication avenues opened between the sciences and the new scholarship in the humanities and social sciences, we will not, she cautions, end the "sanctioning of female ignorance about matters scientific."

Supporting Fausto-Sterling's call, Sandra Harding (1993, 45-48) also asks that we further explore "the causal relation between women's disinterest in the sciences and the sciences' disinterest in their social histories." Sue Rosser (1993, 192) also argues that "attention must be paid to curricular content and teaching techniques traditionally used in mathematics, science, and engineering to determine how they might be changed to be more attractive" to underrepresented groups and that doing so would ultimately produce better science.

These clarion calls address two different but complementary narratives, each of which has dominated discussions about gender and science in the last half of the twentieth century. The first one concerns women *in* science: How can things be done differently to increase the numbers of women who study science, math, and engineering? The second one concerns women *and* science: How will the new scholarship about women and gender alter science itself and how science is understood both within its own disciplines and beyond?

The first story is better known. After three decades of attention, serious progress has been made in this area, though that progress is not yet sufficient, as Angela Ginorio's and Marjorie Olmstead's article in this volume, "Issues for Ethnic Minorities and Women in Science and Engineering," attests. The "Study on the Status of Women Faculty in Science at MIT," released in 2000, documented entrenched patterns of inequities for women faculty in the sciences, underscoring the pervasiveness and difficulty of the task still before higher education. Nonetheless, at the national, state, and local levels, new resources have been allocated to address the embarrassing and troubling underrepresentation of girls and women in science. The National Science Foundation, professional societies for various disciplines, and the K-12 community, among others, have weighed in with intervention strategies and a determination to change things. Mentoring programs, summer bridge programs, and special research opportunities have been established to overcome and eliminate conscious and unconscious discouragement of women and girls in science. New teaching approaches have been adopted to increase outreach to all students. Gradually the numbers have begun to shift, though unevenly for various racial and ethnic populations, for girls and women, and within different science disciplines. Angela B. Ginorio's *Warming the Climate for Women in Academic Science* (1995) is a succinct distillation of what has been learned about access, retention, and success during this period of experimentation.

The second story has been made possible in part because the numbers did shift and in part because of three decades of feminist scholarship. It has been aided as well by the establishment of more than 640 women's studies programs since 1970. By some accounts, the formation of the Boston Women's Health Collective and its now classic *Our Bodies/Ourselves* (1971) mark the activist origin linking women and science. Its more purely academic origins dramatically surfaced with the increase in the numbers of women students and professors in science and with the incorporation of science questions into feminist scholarship, especially through several high profile books and articles in the mid-1980s. The implications of these convergences are just now being felt, their full potential barely suggested. Hence, the sensation of being in unfamiliar territory just as Buster the Crab found himself. If the increase in women's participation in science is primarily about improving access and climate, the growing scholarship about women, gender, and science is primarily about content.

Together these two narratives have become intertwined to form a new area of scholarship. Like all fields, especially emerging ones, it is characterized by heterogeneity, robust debates, and contested ideas even within its own circle of practitioners. Feminist science studies, however, is emerging as the collective term for this burgeoning field produced by scientists and non-scientists alike. It is typically understood to be part of what is called science studies.

Scientific Literacy and Feminist Science Studies

"AMERICA HAS PRODUCED A significant share of the world's great scientists while most of its population is virtually illiterate in science," argued the National Science Foundation in its 1996 report, *Shaping the Future: New Expectations for Undergraduate Education in Science, Mathematics, Engineering, and Technology*. Many in this scientifically illiterate population hold college degrees. Having settled for a system geared towards training a small percentage of students for postgraduate study in the sciences and largely ignoring the rest, higher education has contributed to this embarrassing state of affairs. The urgency of valuing scientific literacy as a core competency in a robust democracy has been brought home by a world saturated by technology, threatened by environmental degradation, and dominated by numbers.

The academy has been trying for some years to reverse the mass of scientifically illiterate individuals. The assumption that scientific reasoning is available to a broad range of people, an interest in the hands-on practice of science, and the sheer delight in exploring scientific questions have all emerged as compelling strategies in the 1990s. As such, scientists echo what was actually far more common practice in nineteenth-century America. Today, however, more may be at stake. Scientific literacy is not merely learning a pre-ordained set of scientific facts. Contemporary science is a matter of understanding how science helps us to interpret the universe, what makes its observations tenable, and what issues it cannot address. This project suggests that to be scientifically literate is to be able to ask intelligent questions about scientific claims, to explore a scientific question with some fullness on one's own and collectively, and to make informed judgments along the way.

Socialized to avoid science and mathematics and often tolerated only as temporary guests when they make their way there, more women than men steer clear of formal science; they are also quicker than most men to say that they don't do well in math, even when they do. In colleges, they have limited their horizons by avoiding science and mathematics courses in disproportionate numbers and resisted exploring scientific questions within their non-science curriculum. Women have read the societal signals that it is okay not to know science.

Feminist science studies scholars and this project seek to challenge such attitudes. They challenge science departments to teach to and about women, and they challenge those who teach non-science courses to embed scientific questions throughout the undergraduate curriculum. *Women and Scientific Literacy: Building Two-Way Streets* is urging women to take science seriously whether or not they are science majors, to learn how it orders and explores the world, and to question it along the way. For many women, but also for a good number of men, feminist science studies provides a way to reclaim the scientist within: the curious mind that likes patterns, wonders how things work, observes the world attentively, and delights in finding relational causes and links.

Feminist science studies argues that such a reclamation is fostered by opening up science to new questions, questions that might grow out of history or ethics, economics or religion, art or business. It defines science in context, not as a disconnected, ethereal body of knowledge, but rather, as something deeply rooted in the world itself, in all its messiness. Feminist science studies sees science as something that matters profoundly to men and women alike. Feminist science studies scholars look for ways to comprehend the sometimes mystifying connections between science and what an average citizen might call ordinary life. It also assumes that a thoughtful, observant person can ask a good question about science and, in the process of searching for or evaluating the answer, can, in fact, become scientifically literate.

Feminist Science Studies and Science Education Reform

FEMINIST SCIENCE STUDIES AND the broader movement to reform science education have much in common. Each shares a commitment to increasing student access and success in the sciences, to improving how science is taught, and to bringing the context of science into the science classroom, in large part through interdisciplinary thinking. What distinguishes them from one another is the rationale that serves as the driving force for reform and the relationship of the various reforms to their final goals.

RATIONALE

Most science education reformers, for example, believe that science research and practice are fundamentally sound, but education about science is poor. Science is unblemished and objective, the argument runs; it simply needs to be taught better. Feminist science studies scholars, on the other hand, believe that science research and practice, though excellent in many respects, are limited by their lack of understanding of the role that social variables play at different levels of scientific inquiry, including their methods and research practices. Feminist science studies practitioners and scholars believe that science can become even better by attending to these issues. The very kind of thinking that will improve the content of science, they argue, is the kind of thinking each professor needs to foster in students: critical thinking, problem-solving, engagement with real world issues. For feminist science studies practitioners, then, good teaching flows directly from intellectual questions about the content, meaning, contextual analysis, purposes, and practice of science.

UNDERREPRESENTATION

Many drawn into science education reform are disturbed by the noticeable underrepresentation of white women and men and women of color in science and technology fields. The concern is motivated by practical and economic considerations as well as by issues of justice and equality. A major report published in 1996 by the National Science Foundation suggested that if the United States hopes to produce an adequate number of scientists, it is important to attract underrepresented populations of women and minorities to science. New research has focused on obstructions in the educational pipeline. At what key points in K-16 education do women and minorities stop taking science and math courses? What explains the high attrition rates for those who opt for science? What attracts women and minorities to science and what helps them thrive when they choose to stay?

Like science education reformers, feminist science studies practitioners care deeply about the access and success questions. Most have played important roles in new research, campus programming, and mentoring projects, all of which have helped to increase the numbers of white women and women and men of color in the sciences. Feminist science studies, however, is pushing beyond the issue of enrollment to questions about the content of science courses; practitioners believe that more women will be attracted to, remain in, and succeed in science when the knowledge base incorporates a gender analysis.

STUDENT-CENTERED

Redesigning how science is taught became a rallying cry of science reformers after research confirmed that overall science and mathematics teaching was of such poor quality that it was a key factor in driving out many students. Science courses were seen as dull, their climate intimidating, and the required lab work mechanical and with little relation to course lectures or the actual practices and realities of day-to-day science. The professors were judged as more focused on their research than on student learning. They also seemed fixed on weeding out students rather than helping them succeed (NSF 1996).

Science education reformers set out on a course of reforms dear to the heart of feminist science studies practitioners. Both groups value student-centered classrooms where the cognitive and intellectual development of the student is a key goal; where active, engaged, participatory learning is the common mode; where problem solving, often in groups, teaches teamwork and better communication; and where recognition that every student has a contribution to make is considered in measuring what a student has learned. A commitment to empowering students and making productive educational use of what they already know has gone hand-in-hand with the development of women's studies and new scholarship in feminist science studies. Good teaching is not enough, however. Feminist science studies aims not only to facilitate student learning, but also to produce better science.

IN CONTEXT

Some of the most exciting new science courses have resulted from reforms that have placed science in context. Believing that learning is enhanced if students understand the relationship between abstract ideas and real-world applications, courses have been redesigned around contemporary themes and issues, and practical, applied projects. Students learn science in order to solve a problem or illuminate a troubling question. In organizing knowledge this way, many science courses have become interdisciplinary and have revolutionized science curricula and unsettled some instructors accustomed to covering a set amount of information within prescribed boundaries.

Because a representative body of feminist science studies argues for the importance of seeing science in context, its scholars have invested significant effort in helping people understand that science is neither detached from nor uninfluenced by history, politics, or economics. Hence, it is unwilling to claim that science, unlike other fields of knowledge, is purely objective, without bias, and unfettered by a material world. In fact, understanding how deeply rooted in the world science itself is becomes a critical way to understand how science actually works, how its theories and practices influence society, and how students, themselves, can use their science training to evaluate science claims and advance scientific knowledge. This kind of thinking leads feminist science studies practitioners to join with other science education reformers to explore connections, relationships, and influences and to argue for more interdisciplinary and multi-disciplinary approaches.

AAC&U's Women and Scientific Literacy Project

COMMITTED TO SCIENCE EDUCATION reform, convinced that scientific literacy was an achievable goal, and courageous enough to plunge into a new body of scholarship, more than seventy-five colleges and universities applied for the ten slots available in *Women and Scientific Literacy*. Each institutional team was originally composed of four scientists and two non-scientists, although by the end of the project, most schools had expanded the numbers greatly. The project was guided throughout by an advisory board of scientists (see Appendix B for full listing) who also functioned as consultants to the participating institutions. AAC&U organized two national conferences for project participants and the campus teams were to design faculty development opportunities at their own schools over a three-year period as well. The expectation was that eventually the immersion into the new scholarship on gender and science would lead to new courses both within and beyond science disciplines.

At the first gathering of the group in Tempe, Arizona, the difficulty and the exhilaration of the task quickly became apparent. By day two, some scientists demanded more overheads and bullets and fewer words. Hierarchies among even the science disciplines or the fields within certain science disciplines surfaced. Different disciplines had varying assumptions about what constituted evidence. Vocabularies were sometimes confusing or impenetrable. On occasion, people talked past one another. It was almost as if it was an international conference where utterly different languages were spoken and there were not enough translators available.

But there were moments when unexpected correspondences surfaced between an historian and a physicist, or an English professor and a biologist. Small group seminars had been organized to introduce participants to a taste of the new scholarship in feminist science studies. Because everyone needed some assistance in crossing disciplinary divides, people began to find ways to describe their fields so outsiders could become insiders, of a sort. A riveting lecture by Anne Fausto-Sterling galvanized the group. When she found herself teaching an embryology course after a several-year hiatus, she realized that her definition of the boundary lines of science had so expanded in the intervening years that she needed to redesign the course. She described the difficulty she had reconceptualizing and then figuring out how in the world to teach a revised embryology course that incorporated arresting new interdisciplinary ideas and participatory pedagogies. Dynamics at the meeting noticeably shifted as a result of her talk. Spurred on to tackle this exciting new field, people began to create a collective bibliography mapping new intellectual territories, and institutional teams committed themselves to constructing websites to capture the unfolding process at each of the campuses.

Still, the tension had been palpable and the uneasiness visible. This is when the story of Buster the Crab became an especially important fable for the group. Buster's own pluckiness and adaptability inspired people to move into unfamiliar areas and plunge over the edge, even when they might not really want to. It turns out that hermit crabs periodically get themselves in just the kind of fix the project participants were in: They outgrow the houses in which they live. The good news is that by molting, crabs can, as Kingsolver describes it, shuck off their old casing and "split themselves open…and start life over with a fresh skin, complete with new appendages and even—if need be—whole regenerated eyes." The bad news is that the process makes the crab vulnerable—as in a deliciously edible soft-shelled crab enjoyed by humans and gulls alike. Predictably such vulnerability can make the crustacean, well, a bit crabby. Quoting a guidebook on hermit-crab care by Neal Pronck, Kingsolver describes the crab's unstable mental state when it is exposed and cut off from its former protective shell covering: "They'll start having nervous breakdowns…They want those shells, and they'll do everything in their power to make sure that they don't get cut off from them. Pinch, scratch, smash, kill—whatever" (264).

Understanding the perfectly natural responses of the hermit crab to its sudden state of vulnerability helped project participants to be patient with their own disequilibrium as they, too, cast off their own familiar if confining constructions. They also understood that it is only through the process of molting that the hermit crab can grow larger. Seeking "whole regenerated eyes," participants took a deep breath and, almost to a person, emerged by the end of three-year's time living in intellectually more spacious chambers.

Gender, Science, and the Undergraduate Curriculum Anthology

THE FOLLOWING ESSAYS GIVE only a partial glimpse of just how roomy the quarters can be. Many of the authors talk about how they had to go outside of their traditional training to do this work, a risk that proved to be both exhilarating and nerve-wracking. The process was also gradual for most—one section of a syllabus or one course at a time. Others plunged right into the sea of scholarship in feminist science studies. Some came to the scholarship first through the door of pedagogy. They began by improving how science is taught.

In Part 1 of the anthology, New Courses and New Intellectual Frameworks, a series of authors in both science and non-science disciplines describe the process in more detail. Sharon Kinsman, for example, created an entirely new course, "Life, Sex, and Cells," which was cross-listed in both biology and women's studies. She wanted to show "how scientific content and feminist approaches can be woven together" to explore some critical questions: "How did sex evolve? What are, and what explains, the characteristics of sex and reproduction in many species?" Though at first unsettled by the course, the science majors came to see how science could be improved by critique; and the non-science majors came to take pride in their newly acquired abilities to translate and evaluate scientific research studies.

In Thomas Wenzel's essay, "General Chemistry: Expanding the Goals Beyond Content and Lab Skills," he explains how his participation in a semester-long faculty development seminar at Bates College in feminist science studies reinforced his investment in developing more participatory, student-centered cooperative pedagogies as a way to engage non-majors in chemistry. But it also persuaded him to design his courses so students could "examine open-ended questions that do not have established answers, and consider science in a social and cultural context."

Trained as an historian, Katrin Schultheiss at the University of Illinois, Chicago, built her two-way street by integrating science into the introductory and theoretical courses within women's studies. Her essay shows the challenge of trying to demystify science for women's studies faculty. Even more importantly, she points out that non-scientifically trained women's studies faculty "can make an important contribution to students' understanding of science not in spite of their lack of scientific training, but because of their familiarity with feminist theory."

The final essay in this section, "Issues in Women's Health: An Interdisciplinary Experience," by Maria Tahamont, Janet Moore Lindman, and Virginia Brown represents the successful converging of people from across disciplinary divides who meet and linger on the two-way streets. A biologist, an historian, and a psychologist combine at Rowan University to "examine women's health issues in their social, cultural, and historical contexts," "understand the biology underlying women's health and illness," and "analyze the gendered assumptions" repeatedly made about women's health. The experience, they argue, was positive for their students and positive professionally for the faculty.

In Part 2 of the anthology the focus shifts from intellectual frameworks to Policy and Pedagogy. The first two essays squarely address Science, Social Policy, and Student Learning; the last two attend more explicitly to *The Classroom as Laboratory: Teaching Strategies* and *Student Reactions*. Angela Ginorio and Marjorie Olmstead in "Issues for Ethnic Minorities and Women in Science and Engineering," like the Rowan professors, team taught their course. A women's studies professor trained in psychology joined with a physicist in a cross-listed course. However, they adopted a different entry point into scientific questions. Using issues faced by ethnic minorities and women in science and engineering nationally and locally, students paired the research data with opportunities through the course to meet experts in the field and to apply critical feminist analyses to the topics under study. In a move that was new to both professors, they decided not only to include a policy dimension to the course but to require students "to identify a pressing issue and then develop a policy recommendation to present a decision maker at the local, state, or national level."

The results were quite astonishing. At the end of the course, the class followed the format of their own final reports and "documented the local issues at the University of Washington, provided data relevant to each, and offered a series of recommendations." This end-of-the-course report was presented in person to the president, key deans, and all science chairs in the college of arts and sciences. "Since presenting our report, 20 percent of the recommendations have been implemented and work is ongoing on some of the others."

The University of Rhode Island (URI) project had a similarly impressive outcome for students and faculty members alike who came to believe they could indeed influence particular aspects of their lives by amassing scientific data and understanding the political context of an issue. Ten URI authors have composed a powerful institutional narrative in "The Curriculum in Context: Campus Networks and Change." They demonstrate powerfully that, "the curriculum doesn't exist in isolation" but is the "product of the lives and work of faculty, students, and administrators. Thus, the curriculum evolves in a context of networks of people, a climate for new ideas and practices, and even the physical buildings and infrastructure of the campus."

The essay tracks how strong networks of women faculty first organized in parallel networks, first as a group of women's studies professors and as a group of women scientists. Eventually these two groups began to work together through *Women and Scientific Literacy*. Finally, an even more encompassing network, the Women's Equity Committee, was established to address pressing policy issues campus wide. The first issue the Committee focused on involved a "toxic environment" for the three women professors in the sixty-eight person college of engineering. The second involved the (literally) toxic environment in the main science building where seven women between 1992-1994 were diagnosed with breast cancer and an eighth one in 1996. Both issues become the context from which a variety of new URI courses emerged in feminist science studies.

Eventually after relevant data had been gathered and external agencies had been brought in to examine the situation, the dean of the college of engineering was replaced and a series of recommendations made to assure a more hospitable environment for women students and faculty. Similarly, after a careful scientific study was at last completed, and when levels of PCBs eight times the normal amount were found, the science building in question was immediately evacuated and closed. Finally, after Dana Shugar in women's studies and English died of breast cancer, her students honored her by creating a group research project on breast cancer and the environment in Rhode Island which they published in the spring of 2000.

Moving from policy to pedagogy, Catherine Middlecamp and Banu Subramaniam from the University of Wisconsin-Madison and University of Arizona respectively, offer their essay, "What is Feminist Pedagogy? Useful Ideas for Teaching Chemistry." After elaborating on the terminology, they discuss themes common to feminist pedagogies such as voice, empowerment, authority, and positionality, followed by very practical ideas to use in chemistry classes. They conclude, "Feminist pedagogy can benefit all students. It calls for an increase in our openness to ideas from students, a willingness to change materials or styles if these can benefit student learning, and a way to make a place for the new knowledge and connections that students can bring to a course."

In "Gender and Science Across the Curriculum: Students Respond," four professors at the University of Arizona from four different disciplines pose the question, "What does it mean to introduce issues of gender and science across the curriculum? How are students in different fields responding to these curricular transformations?"

Each professor sought individually to foster what they called "gender literacy." Laura Briggs wanted her women's studies courses to "empower students to fear no science, to communicate an enthusiasm for the possibilities of scientific ways of knowing, and to teach tools for analyzing sexist and racist science." Sharla Fett in history sought in her course to "explore deeply the entrenched issues of power and justice in African-American health, while at the same time rejecting a monolithic conspiratorial view of biomedical institutions."

Jennifer Croissant, one of nine women out of 150 faculty members in the college of engineering, had the most difficult task of the four. In the context of "Introduction to Engineering," she could introduce only fairly neutral material on promotion and social responsibility in the workplace. By contrast, a first year colloquium, "Women in Science and Engineering," which drew 70 percent female students, could be explicitly about gender. Marta Civil in mathematics focused primarily on pedagogical strategies through which she "listens to students construct meaning in mathematics," which in turn sparked her interest in ethnomathematics. She found overall that "it is in the teaching approaches rather than content where changes could occur most productively in her field." While students were affected in all four disciplines, there was a general consensus that students in women's studies courses were much more receptive to the introduction of science than students in science courses were to the introduction of gender into science.

The anthology's conclusion ends by answering some frequently asked questions about feminist science studies. Some typical questions are: What is meant by feminist, and what does it have to do with science? What is feminist science studies, and how did it originate? Does feminist science studies suggest a form of relativism where all perspectives are "right"? Since it is sometimes critical of existing scientific paradigms and practices, won't feminist science studies discourage women from pursuing science?

Appendixes include a sampling of the range of courses created during the project to integrate content about women and gender into the content of science courses and new questions about science into non-science courses. A more expansive collection of syllabi can be found on AAC&U's website for the project at www.aacu-edu.org/Initiatives/scilit.html. Almost all of the ten participating institutions also have web sites on their home pages linked to the AAC&U website. In each of those sites, an even more complete record of courses and project activities can be found.

Closing Comments

IF PROJECT PARTICIPANTS WERE uneasy in Tempe, Arizona when they first tiptoed into this hybrid called feminist science studies, students reflect similar twin responses of discomfort and elation. The University of Arizona article below describes the resistance that many students initially have, particularly science students. But for many students, taking one of the feminist science studies courses turns them into versions of a hermit crab. They discover that they, like Buster the Crab, can indeed regenerate whole new eyes. As a Bates student so succinctly captures it, "This class has made me see the world and myself differently. I'm not afraid of science anymore." Similarly, a Rowan student asserts, "This class was my favorite ever. I loved coming to class every Wednesday, and even wanted to continue class discussions outside of class...I want the rest of the world to learn what we did."

The University of Arizona authors summarize what was a theme in all of the participating project campuses: "As a result of these classes, students, sometimes despite themselves, take science more seriously as a cultural product and a resource for their own personal and professional lives. They also take science less seriously as a hegemonic discourse. They now question expertise and evidence in thoughtful and productive ways." As they ponder these findings, the University of Arizona authors realize that what the project has stimulated is "a reinvention of the liberal arts in its most progressive modes. Valuing the traditions of open inquiry, diverse perspectives, and collegial discourses, we experience the pedagogical power of liberal inquiry as applied to and combined with what we see as the best of science." In the process, these ten NSF-funded institutions have begun to make progress toward remedying a dilemma Anne Fausto-Sterling raised almost a decade ago. These fearless inquirers were willing to tap-tap-tap their way to the edge of the precipice and despite the sudden dislocation of an unfamiliar world, they managed to find their balance. Because they did, they have helped us all get closer to the day in which science will be a legitimate place for women, and gender studies will be an appropriate enterprise for scientists.

Works Cited

Fausto-Sterling, Anne. Fall 1992. Building two-way streets: The case of feminism and science. *NWSA Journal,* 4: 3, 336-349.

Harding, Sandra. Spring 1993. Forum: Feminism and science. *NWSA Journal,* 5: 1, 45-48.

Kingsolver, Barbara. 1995. *High tide in Tucson: Essays from now and never.* New York: Harper Collins Publishers.

National Science Foundation. 1996. Shaping the future: New expectations for undergraduate education in science, mathematics, engineering, and technology. Washington, DC: National Science Foundation.

Rosser, Sue. 1993. Female friendly science: Including women in curricular content and pedagogy in science. *Journal of General Education,* 42: 3, 191-220.

Part one

New Courses and
New Intellectual Frameworks

Transforming Courses in
Science and Women's Studies

Life, Sex, and Cells

Sharon Kinsman

For a decade, I taught undergraduate courses in biology and evolutionary ecology in conventional ways. But recently, I developed a rather unconventional course about current understandings of the evolution and consequences of sex. The biological content, feminist critiques, and teaching methods I employed were outside of my traditional training, and represented dramatic changes in my teaching. I designed "Life, Sex, and Cells"—simultaneously a core course in women's students and introductory course in biology—to encourage students to be curious about detailed scientific content and feminist science studies and to use content and analysis together to investigate certain questions about sex and reproduction. I deliberately chose these questions not just because they are likely to interest young adults, but because they can lead to interesting, instructive queries about how science is done, how popular culture uses science, and to questions, assumptions, methods, and conclusions. The venture for me was exhilarating and nerve-wracking; the payoffs for students included some I had not anticipated. For instance, one student noted:[1]

> This class has made me see the world and myself differently. I am not afraid of science anymore. I feel like I can have a conversation with someone about biology and not run away in fear. I realize that things I learned growing up about science can be argued as not necessarily "true" as I once thought it to be. You have opened my mind to a subject I have neglected for too long.

Feminist approaches to science that I had come to embrace for my own research motivated me to design this course. This personal and professional journey had begun for me years earlier, in the course of my research in plant reproductive ecology. In closely examining research literature on questions about pollination and fertilization of flowering plants, I discovered certain unexamined problems with the fields' paradigms, practices, and presentations. Feminist scholars helped me see that it is not unusual to examine science as a cultural endeavor that is not as objective as I had been trained to believe. Using feminist scholarship, I began to reexamine my field and, as a result, my approach to science changed: I now recognize how crucial it is to use and assess content (or what we call the "facts" of science) along with both "feminist" and "scientific" critiques of science. Putting into practice a feminist approach to science in my research has strongly motivated me to change what and how I teach.

In this chapter, I focus on the framework and methods of "Life, Sex and Cells," using selected examples of course content as illustrations. I hope to characterize a potential example of how scientific content and feminist approaches can be woven together to make sense for us and our students.

Why Sex? Content and Critique

SEX—THE MIXING OF DNA of two distinct individuals—is the unifying theme of "Life, Sex, and Cells." In teaching, and in this chapter, I use *sex* to mean "DNA mixing." Otherwise, I use *"sex,"* referring to one of the more common uses of the word, such as shorthand for "sexual reproduction," or for acts such as copulation that bring gametes close together. On occasion, I use the term *DNA mixing* in place of the word *sex,* as a reminder of the most basic definition.

Understanding sex—whether its biological role or its cultural representations or misrepresentations—compels learning both content and critique. Thus we examine not just the biology of sex, but *how* biologists approach and write about its origins, patterns, and consequences. Sex is an exceptionally good topic for students beginning to learn biological concepts and detail ("content") because investigating its biological role requires knowledge of cell structure and function, cell evolution, genetics, evolutionary biology, development of multicellular organisms, biological diversity, and behavior. But understanding sex also demands critical analysis—especially cultural and feminist critiques—not only because "sex" has multiple and confusing definitions and representations, but because its biological meaning and role often are misrepresented or explored only for a limited set of the species, even in biological literature.

The two central questions of the course—How did sex originate and evolve? What are, and what explains, the characteristics of sex and reproduction in the many species?—provide many opportunities to identify the limitations of their popular explanations, and to explore why popular explanations reflect only a few selected species and only some of the many patterns of sex and reproduction. Our work in "Life, Sex, and Cells" suggests that these popular explanations and the narrow scientific approaches they reflect significantly limit our knowledge and understanding of the diverse patterns of sex and reproduction and their early cellular origins.

Our journey in "Life, Sex, and Cells" is toward more broadly informed views of sex, of reproduction, of the species, and especially of science itself. Implicitly and explicitly, I ask the students to use the two central topics—the origin of sex and the patterns and consequences of sex—to consider the following questions: What constitutes knowledge, and who creates it? What are the mainstream ideas, and why have they come to be favored? What shapes and what constitutes an explanatory paradigm, and what kinds of evidence are put forth to support it? Why is this particular evidence emphasized? How are the "knowledge," the "evidence," and the "explanation" presented to us? How does this presentation affect our learning, our reasoning, our questions, and our conclusions? Can we improve the presentation, the paradigm, and the evidence? Can we find or create different points of view?

These questions, first implicit, then explicit, underlie a good deal of our daily work. They lead students to identify and to question various popular characterizations of sex (for example, the idea that sex evolved *because* variation in offspring is good) and of the reproductive practices often linked to sex (for example, the idea that males "naturally" should be promiscuous). Our work requires linking content with critique, and students' accomplishments demonstrate that science can be improved by critique and that critique based in scientific literacy can be particularly strong and insightful. By learning substantial content in order to understand and create critique, students become able to discover what the paradigms are missing, and to evaluate the paradigms' evidence and consequences. I want students to understand that all of us can contribute to (or at least assess) what constitutes the questions, kinds of evidence, and breadth of approaches for any particular "scientific" question. I insist on the difficult work that this eventually requires. We begin with more accessible tasks: defining sex and discovering its diverse, intriguing forms.

Beginning with Basics: Definitions and Diversity

TO BEGIN THE COURSE, students must recognize multiple meanings for *sex, reproduction,* and *gender,* and become familiar with the variety of characteristics of sex and reproduction to be found among the species. They must use this information in considering the natural world and the ways humans try to make sense of the natural world. In sorting out the many ways that the words *sex* and *reproduction* are used and linked, we begin to learn about biology and representations of sex. For example, we learn that sex is most fundamentally defined as DNA mixing between individuals (Margulis and Sagan 1986). Bacteria mix DNA in conjugation, and gametes such as pollen and ovules mix DNA when fertilization occurs. We find that reproduction is not sex (and that sex is not reproduction). Reproduction means making additional independent organisms called offspring. While many species make these offspring sexually, not all reproduction requires sex. Species that clone reproduce without DNA mixing. Many plants make offspring from fragments that take root, and certain species of lizards and insects that have no males reproduce parthenogenetically: the females make daughters from unfertilized eggs. Similarly, sex does not require reproduction. That is, DNA mixing between individuals (such as conjugation in bacteria) can occur with no subsequent production of offspring.

Sex occurs, we find, at least intermittently or for some individuals, in a majority of the 30 million or so unicellular (for example, bacteria, protozoa, and diatoms) and multicellular (for example, plants, fungi, and animals) species. This DNA mixing began with early cells. Some biologists who study cell evolution suggest that sex then became (perhaps by accident) inextricably associated with many features of organisms, including DNA repair (Michod 1995), cell structure, the multicellular condition, and the ways that multicellular individuals develop through cell differentiation (Margulis and Sagan 1986). These links may have forced certain reproductive mechanisms also to become associated with sex, particularly in multicellular organisms (Margulis and Sagan 1986) In brief, DNA mixing may not be for reproduction, even though it is now linked to reproduction (and to many other conditions) in many species.

Students see that these fundamental views of the definition and origin of *sex* are not mainstream in biology; many biologists who have studied and written about "sex" actually address not sex per se but reproduction that is sexual. Indeed, *sex* has come (erroneously) to mean "reproduction" in popular views and to many biologists and often implicitly refers only to animals with backbones. Furthermore, ideas of gender are conjoined with ideas about sex and reproduction. Thus we find that our popular vocabulary, even our scientific vocabulary, is imprecise. To know what we are talking about in class, we must define terms that usually are used imprecisely, and we must restate our meanings repeatedly. In class we address the confusing terms and their fundamental definitions, coming to see that their conceptual linkages are not surprising: in the species we are most familiar with, reproduction usually *is* associated with DNA mixing and with structures or individuals labeled "female" (having large nutritious gametes such as plants' ovules or animals' eggs) and "male" (having small gametes such as plants' pollen or animals' sperm).

Indeed, in our recent mammalian lineage, sex is inflexibly linked with reproduction and with distinct female and male conditions. No wonder we are not inclined to think about what sex really means, how it got started, and the implications of its original distinction from reproduction.

Thus our struggle to understand "sex" and "reproduction" also demands familiarity with biological diversity—particularly of the diversity and flexibility of sexual and reproductive patterns among the millions of other species. Mammals' rigid—perhaps originally accidental—coincidence of DNA mixing and reproduction (along with distinct individual female and male conditions) is far from the only pattern to be found in the array of all species. Let flowering plants frame the way one makes sense of the natural world (as I do), and the picture broadens. Flowering plants are incomparably varied in mechanisms that bring about DNA mixing, in the distribution of male and female reproductive structures within and among individual organisms of a species (for example, functional hermaphroditism is very common), and in breeding systems (for example, many are self-fertile). Many can clone (make offspring nonsexually), switch back and forth between biological male and female reproductive conditions, abort selectively, mate simultaneously with multiple partners, and employ other species (the birds and the bees, the bats and the beetles) to bring their gametes close together prior to sex. Considering the flowering plants alone, it's not a dull world!

Toss in the bacteria, the obscure but diverse protista (for example, diatoms, amoebas, algae), insects, marine invertebrates, and certain fishes: now the patterns of sex and reproduction burgeon to a truly riveting array. Just a sample might include hermaphroditic slugs and roundworms, fish that change from male to female, aphids and other invertebrates animals that rampantly clone, sister societies of yellow jackets and bees, intermittent DNA mixing triggered by shrinking body size in diatoms, pregnant male pipefish, female-only species of insects and fish, and female insects that make egg yolk from fatty sperm packets collected from males. These intriguing phenomena—often treated by popular literature as anomalies or "just so" stories—are strands of a colorful tapestry of a variety of norms.

Because most of us are not familiar with the species, and with the diverse patterns of DNA mixing and reproduction they embody, our struggles to understand humans (and especially human dilemmas about "sex," "gender," and "sexual orientation") are impoverished. Our students, I think, need to know about the flowering plants, the fishes, the aphids, and the gulls. Shouldn't a fish whose gonads can be first male, then female, help us determine what constitutes "male" and "female"? Shouldn't an aphid fundatrix ("stem mother") inform our ideas of "mother"? There on the rose bush, she neatly copies herself, depositing minuscule, sap-siphoning, genetically identical daughters. Aphids might lead us to ask not "Why do they clone?" but "Why don't we?" Shouldn't the long-term female homosexual pair bonding in certain species of gulls (Bagemihl 1999) help define our views of successful parenting, and help students reflect on the intersection of social norms and biology? I want students to adopt a broad view of sex and reproduction based on biological diversity. I ask them to peer into aphid colonies with interest. I insist that they inform their investigation of sex, reproduction, and gender, and of the ways that biologists approach and present these topics, with knowledge of the diversity of sexual and reproductive ways among the multiplicity of species of all lineages.

Learning Methods: Expectations and Environment

WHILE THE FIRST TOPICS—definitions and diversity—provide a framework for investigating sex, the first class meetings set expectations for very active learning. Students can best practice the kind of learning and application I expect via the wide variety of pedagogical techniques often called "feminist." Learning from my women's studies colleagues, I (nervously but successfully) dispense with exams and frequent lectures, and use teaching methods that emphasize participation, reflection, and explanation in lively interactions that involve everyone.

I emphasize participation because I want students to be comfortable thinking about, evaluating, and applying content. With twenty to forty students per section, who represent many majors and all four college years, participation works well. Our work with basic definitions and with biological diversity provides good examples. In the first class meeting, good-willed laughter ensues when we share some of our written definitions of *sex, reproduction,* and *gender.* I give students tacit permission to express a variety of responses by asking them to identify the most surprising, or unbelievable, or unattractive method of intimacy their reading presents. Our class review of the varied ways animals bring eggs and sperm close together prior to DNA mixing (Kevles 1986) models matter-of-fact discussion of potentially embarrassing topics and terms. In identifying themes revealed by these examples of animals' intimacies, we also review animal diversity, concluding that a wide variety of reproductive practices are, simply, "normal."

Participatory learning works very well. One student commented: "There was no way to hide in the corner because a great deal of participation was necessary and encouraged." The payoff in their confidence is especially obvious later, when small groups must design an efficient design for meiosis (the type of cell division that reduces the number of chromosomes per cell). Their insights and responses are impressive. The students' ownership and participation are so effective that they complain outright that books have never taught them to think about the fact that mechanisms of cell division are constrained because they evolved from earlier conditions. This kind of confident questioning soon embraces critique. We often ask "why": Why are there two states—female and male—and not three? Why do we have the ideas we do of "female" and "male" animals? Why has the astonishing variety of "sexual" and reproductive patterns deviating from the heterosexual "norm" been described forthrightly only recently (Bagemihl 1999)? Why do aphids clone, while humans do not? Why is functional hermaphroditism absent in most vertebrates, and how does this affect our representations and views of hermaphroditism?

Just as participation encourages critical thinking, so do close reading and responsible writing. For nearly every reading, students must answer questions that demand that they learn the scientific content, consider carefully the material and the author's intent, and use information from earlier classes. Culminating writing assignments similarly emphasize detailed learning and responsibility. Students write short passages designed for college biology textbooks and chapters for popular books, as well as analytical reviews that demand substantial knowledge and well-supported argument. Ideally, writing to educate others helps students understand that this field, and "science" as a whole, is an accessible human endeavor strongly influenced by culture and by individuals.

Introducing Critique: Conceptions of Conception[2]

IN ORDER TO INTRODUCE analyses of content and critique, we turn to internal fertilization in animals. Students are familiar with popular concepts of fertilization, but are unfamiliar with the idea that presentations of science can be misleading. We begin by reading commentary by primary researchers Heide Schatten and Gerald Schatten (1983) in their article "The Energetic Egg," and evaluating it using Ruth Bleier's (1986) suggestions for standards for "good science."

Next, we turn to learning more about the biology of fertilization (or "content"). We work hard to thoroughly understand current knowledge of the steps in fertilization, reviewing cell types (prokaryotic and eukaryotic) and learning about the structures and functions of the components of eukaryotic cells (such as nuclear envelope, cytoskeleton, membrane, and the processes by which cell parts move and change). In small groups students consult several references, discovering that "scientific" sources can disagree and/or use different emphases, images, and methods. In listing the steps in fertilization, we try to use neutral language and imagery. Vowing to eschew metaphors and stereotypes in their own recounting of fertilization, students come to see that metaphors often are helpful and also see that their choices of metaphors are consequential.

Now, well informed about the biological details, including recent discoveries such as how components of the cytoskeleton are built and disassembled, we return to critique. We read Emily Martin's (1991) or the Biology and Gender Study Group's (1988) accessible, thought-provoking feminist critique of some traditional presentations of egg as passive bride and sperm as competitive, conquering hero. These analyses of classical (often hilarious) depictions of egg and sperm in mammalian fertilization provide concrete examples of the value of a feminist critical approach. The students' detailed knowledge of fertilization means that the critiques are easy to understand—and, in fact, to critique. Most students are very pleased with the power of their scientific literacy. One student commented: "I finally felt like I was learning for the sake of understanding, applying, and building on previous knowledge."

Now the students are well positioned to apply their learning. Specifically, for a college-level biology textbook ("known for accuracy, clarity, and interesting tone"), they write a section that presents an updated, accurate, detailed account of cellular events in mammalian fertilization. The assignment requires explicit revision of outdated, stereotyped depictions of conception. Many of these student papers are outstanding. Even self-confessed "science-phobes" produce excellent work. They learn and use scientific content, act as scientists informed about biases via feminist critiques, and improve science presentation. Their work reflects both the critiques they explore and their sense of having been sold short when they themselves were first taught about fertilization.

Next, we more formally identify our critical approach as feminist, using Ruth Bleier's (1988) "A Decade of Feminist Critique in the Natural Sciences." Bleier sets forth examples of feminist critiques in the form of questions that the students now recognize as tools of analysis. These themes repeat throughout the course as we investigate two larger paradigms and use critiques overt and obscure, feminist and scientific.

Practiced in active learning and in ways to link scientific literacy with critiques to improve science, we turn to the course's two central questions. For the question "How did sex originate and evolve?" we focus on cell biology. In exploring "What are the consequences of sex for the patterns of sex and reproduction?" we focus on the behavior of vertebrate animals.

Origins and Consequences of Sex

THE ORIGIN QUESTION MOST often is linked to what can be called the "why sex?" paradigm. This popular approach implies that sex occurs as a result of the benefit it confers on parents who reproduce sexually: the benefit of genetically varied offspring (quantitatively, a fascinating dilemma of genetic costs and benefits). In its simplest form, the argument implies that sex is good, so species have it. (Note that "sex" by this reasoning is equated or strongly linked with "sexual reproduction.") While this paradigm does suggest how natural selection might *maintain* sex in multicellular lineages with complex bodies, such as the plants and animals, it does not address the *origin* of DNA mixing. To broaden students' understanding, I rely especially on the revolutionary work of Lynn Margulis and Dorion Sagan (1986). Clues about the origin of sex lie in little-known organisms dating from a distant time: especially the bacteria and protista, and their ancestors and early multicellular descendents. Sex probably began as a consequence of peculiarities of the evolution of cells, or DNA, or both, and then seems to have become linked to the demands of multicellularity. We may have sex because we're stuck with it, not because it's good for us. (The genetically varied offspring many species enjoy may be just a serendipitous, albeit sometimes beneficial, side effect of sex having become linked with reproduction.) I aim for students to learn and enjoy the challenging logic of the Margulis and Sagan reasoning and to use this reasoning in concert with literacy about cell biology to critique the "why sex?" paradigm.

Next, we examine the consequences of sex, choosing for particular focus animal behavior and the "parental investment" paradigm. This is an area that has a rich and recent history of feminist approaches and critiques in fields such as primatology and anthropology. We examine the theories of the parental investment (or "Trivers/Bateman") paradigm, which contends that differences in parental investment between females and males both characterize and explain animals' reproductive behavior. As we have done for fertilization, we "decompose" the parental investment model to be sure to understand it and we evaluate the types of evidence offered to support the model. One student remarked, "It made me rethink my ideas about sex and gender, even in terms of humans." Sarah Blaffer Hrdy's (1986) classic essay "Empathy, Polyandry, and the Myth of the Coy Female" is key in modeling how to identify problems with the assumptions, reasoning, and predictions of a theory (in particular, the parental investment model). Having teased apart and understood the components of the parental investment paradigm, students can appreciate and respond to Hrdy's implicit demonstration of how feminist critiques can be built and supported. Students must use their knowledge of the model to identify the assumptions, reasoning, and predictions that Hrdy explicitly challenges. Then, they must explain and judge how she challenges each component, and how she supports each challenge. We discuss who "consumes" science, how this paradigm is used by the popular press, why the popular press is more likely to emphasize the paradigm than to highlight Hrdy's critique, and how work like Hrdy's can empower us to evaluate troubling or limited models.

The students now must synthesize their knowledge of biology and their skills of learning and critique in a difficult assignment. To prepare to write a chapter that could be included in a book on the evolution and consequences of sex, they must "translate" two original research papers that report experimental research on specific questions about mate choice by vertebrate animals. Reading and summarizing primary biological research is entirely new to most. Senior biology majors join us to assist in small learning groups, translating statistics and helping the students understand every detail of the experiments. We review, more than once, each paper's difficult introduction, referring to our schemes of the components of the parental investment paradigm. Students not only must identify each author's central question, they must then explain the question's purported importance, identify the hypothesis and its predictions, and determine the kinds of data that would support the distinct predictions. They must evaluate how well the experiments address the question, and how appropriately the authors use the data.

All of this is quite daunting. I hear a good deal of complaining about the turkeys, guppies, parasites, and pigments we encounter in the mate choice research articles. But then come breakthroughs: Students finally can outline the experiments, and are shocked and pleased when I agree with their suggestions that there are certain faults with the experiments or with the presentation and use of data. They also must come to see the limitations imposed on researchers (in how many replicates can you use a certain guppy?) and to judge whether or not the resulting research is "robust."

Again, hard work to "own" scientific literacy pays off. I am struck by how involved some of the students become. I believe that this is the result of the responsibility they are given: to understand primary research, to judge primary research, and to translate it accurately and competently, without bias, in a theoretical context, for a more general audience.

Coda

FOR MOST STUDENTS, THIS course and the accomplishments and understanding it demands strongly countered their ideas of science and their ideas of their own competence. The few biology majors who took this course had particularly complex reactions. As had been true for me, critiquing their own profession was first scary, then revealing, and finally empowering. One confessed to feeling betrayed by all her earlier biological education and struggled as she continued to be silenced in other science classrooms. Needless to say, I have never had a better classroom teaching experience. I have not yet dramatically changed my other courses, which predate this experiment. But I have colleagues en route who "think that the journey itself [is] worth taking,"[3] and students who remind me that curriculum that integrates science content with feminist analysis is needed throughout science courses: "I was afraid of science because it seemed too much like a truth and a final answer…facts that could never be disputed…I have become aware of so many different components."

Acknowledgments

I AM GRATEFUL TO many individuals for assisting, encouraging, and teaching me: Jean Potuchek, Bonnie Spanier, Scott Gilbert, Lucinda McDade, the editors of this volume [in which this originally appeared], Alice Elliott, pollination biology core-searchers, Suzie and Jane Kinsman, and not least: members of the Bates College [National Science Foundation funded] *Women and Scientific Literacy* project team—Bonnie Shulman, Elizabeth Tobin, Pam Baker, and Georgia Nigro. Funds for developing "Life, Sex, and Cells" were provided by a grant from the Hughes Council of Bates College.

Endnotes

1   All student quotes used in this article are from anonymous evaluations by students enrolled in "Life, Sex, and Cells."

2   Scott Gilbert used this title ("Conceptions of Conceptions") for a talk presented at Bates College.

3   Pamela Baker, Bonnie Shulman, and Elizabeth Tobin. See their chapter, Difficult Crossing: Stories of Building Two-way, in *Feminist Science Studies: A New Generation*. New York, NY: Routledge, Inc.

Works Cited

Bagemihl, Bruce. 1999. *Biological exuberance: Animal homosexuality and natural diversity*. New York: St. Martin's Press.

Biology and Gender Study Group (Sarah Bailey, Athena Beldecos, Scott Gilbert, Karen Hicks, Lori Kenschaft, Nancy Niemczyk, Rebecca Rosenberg, Stephanie Schaertel, and Andrew Wedel). 1998. The importance of feminist critique for contemporary cell biology. *Hypatia*, 3: 61-76.

Bleier, Ruth. 1988. A decade of feminist critique in the natural sciences. *Signs*, 14: 186-195.

_____ (Ed.). 1986. *Feminist approaches to science*. New York: Pergamon Press.

Hrdy, Sarah Blaffer. 1986. Empathy, polyandry, and the myth of the coy female. In R. Bleier, ed. *Feminist approaches to science*. New York: Pergamon Press.

Kevles, Bettyann. 1986. *Females of the species: Sex and survival in the animal kingdom*. Cambridge, MA: Harvard University Press.

Margulis, Lynn, and Dorion Sagan. 1986. *Origins of sex: Three billions years of genetic recombination*. New Haven, CT: Yale University Press.

Martin, Emily. 1991. The egg and the sperm: How science has constructed a romance based on stereotypical male-female roles. *Signs*, 16: 485-501.

Michod, Richard E. 1995. *Eros and evolution: A natural philosophy of sex*. New York: Addison-Wesley Publishing.

Schatten, Gerald, and Heide Schatten. 1983. The energetic egg. *The Sciences*, 23: 28-34.

General Chemistry: Expanding the Goals Beyond Content and Lab Skills

Thomas J. Wenzel

Introduction

Teaching chemistry was relatively easy when I first started. All I had to do was give organized lectures, spiced with enthusiasm and humor, assign reading and homework, use modifications of standard lab experiments gathered from a variety of sources, and I was set. In other words, I taught the same way I was taught.

In my naivete, I did not seriously examine whether my teaching methods best promoted student learning, or whether I was reaching students of different genders, races, or cultural backgrounds. Nor did I ever wonder whether the preponderance of men in chemistry influenced the topics that are taught in general chemistry or their presentation in textbooks and lectures. I did not consider how funding priorities distinguish "important" from "unimportant" questions and are influenced by societal and cultural forces. Whether people's societal or cultural background might affect the interpretation of their scientific investigations never occurred to me. Finally, I could not imagine the possibility of a different science. I am still uncertain whether Western science is a masculine science or whether there could be such a thing as a feminine science. Whereas twenty years ago, I was oblivious to the idea of different sciences, my participation in the National Science Foundation-funded faculty development seminars on the connection between women's studies and science has made me receptive to such a possibility. It also opened my mind to several other issues, each of which has had an impact on my teaching of chemistry.

Early Involvement in General Education

DURING MY FIRST YEAR at Bates, I had team-taught both semesters of our introductory chemistry course for science majors. The next year, when the department needed someone to teach a two-semester general education science requirement for non-majors, I volunteered and taught the course for six years. Many of the students were high achievers with an excellent work ethic who, even though they may not have wanted to take chemistry, wanted to do well in the course. It became obvious that unless the material was relevant to their lives—a goal in which I, too, was interested—attendance would drop considerably. I therefore developed two thematic semesters, one related to environmental chemistry, the other to the chemistry of life. A student who regularly attended the lecture, took good notes, and memorized the material could expect to get A's on the exams. With an enrollment that eventually grew to over 230 students, it was hard to imagine teaching the course any other way.

Returning to the introductory course for science majors after a six-year hiatus, it was eye-opening to examine the lecture notes from my first year of teaching. They were crammed with information, much of which I had no recollection of teaching, some of which I was no longer prepared to teach without prior review. It was difficult to imagine that I actually covered everything in my notes; I certainly could not have "uncovered" the material for the students. It was harder to imagine the students retaining much of significance after the final exam.

That first year, my course had been remarkably similar to what I had experienced as the typical approach to general chemistry. Quantitative material was emphasized, and the solving of quantitative problems was accomplished more by pattern recognition than by actually understanding the concepts. Memorization of facts was emphasized. Many of the topics did not logically connect to each other, a situation exacerbated by the order of material in most general chemistry textbooks. Almost none of the material was presented in a relevant context.

The lab experiments, which I was not responsible for that first year, were one- to two-weeks long. There was no meaningful investigation or discovery. The outcome of experiments was well-known. Lab work was usually done individually, and if done in groups, it did not represent a meaningful cooperative effort. Even when I did have responsibility for designing new experiments later in my teaching, they tended to follow the traditional design of introductory labs. Since the outcomes were expected, most students wanted to minimize the time spent in lab. Understanding the experiment generally assumed secondary importance. Write-ups usually took the form of calculations and brief answers to questions. Data were plugged into predetermined equations with little thought about what the equation or outcome actually meant. When experiments did not work, students and instructors alike were frustrated since the experiments had worked numerous times before and were supposed to work.

When people learn I am a chemistry professor, most express the view that chemistry is a difficult and intimidating subject, relate some negative story from their own educational experience in chemistry, or quickly change the subject. Since most people only take chemistry courses at the introductory level, something about these courses is creating this negative view. That's unfortunate, since such an opinion is bound to inhibit people from becoming chemistry literate.

I believe that several features of the introductory course, besides those already mentioned, contribute to this negative impression. One inherent difficulty is the focus on species (atoms and molecules) that are too small to see, which distances the material from the learner. Laboratory experiments and class demonstrations have also moved away from qualitative and descriptive chemistry, which at least emphasized visual color and state-of-matter changes, toward more theoretical bases of chemistry. Many labs are designed to demonstrate concepts in the lecture rather than to involve students in investigations. Introductory courses emphasize "mature" areas in which chemists have reached consensus on what is factual. As a result, chemistry is presented as a field that studies things that are known.

It is rare in introductory courses for students to examine problems for which solutions are not well established. There is little appreciation of the process scientists use to discover and create knowledge and a lack of historical development within these mature areas to provide an appreciation of the steps, controversies, and differences of opinions that undoubtedly occurred along the path of discovery. The format suggests that there is only one interpretation of data and that the experiments performed and their interpretation are completely independent of a person's societal or cultural background. By emphasizing factual content and quantitative problem solving at the expense of investigation and discovery, chemistry as a discipline is presented as if only experts can make meaningful contributions or ask meaningful questions. No wonder many view the field as incomprehensible and intimidating.

Changes in the Upper-Level Analytical Chemistry Courses

BECAUSE I WANTED STUDENTS to engage with rather than be repelled by chemistry, I began to make a series of significant changes in my upper-level courses. All of these eventually led me to see connections between my goals as a professor and new scholarship emerging out of what is sometimes called feminist science studies. Three factors provided the major impetus for my initial changes. One was an observation that undergraduate students learned things much better in the context of research than in the context of courses, even when simultaneously doing both with me. Material learned in courses seemed to be forgotten in a short time, whereas months later students would speak lucidly about a point that had come up during the course of their research. Somehow they had assumed an ownership and responsibility in their research project that made learning more important and lasting.

A second was the appreciation that the lab experience in my courses was not a realistic representation of analytical chemistry. People who really do analytical chemistry first start by analyzing and defining the problem. When it comes time to perform the analysis, one must then collect samples. Since most samples are complex in nature, it is usually necessary to separate the sought-for constituent from other interfering substances. Only then is it possible to perform the measurement and interpret the data. Most undergraduate analytical labs only consider the last two steps in any detail. Students are given samples and perform the analysis and interpret the data. The most important steps, analyzing and defining the problem, sampling, and pre-separation, are omitted.

The third was a concern that, in lecturing, certain students were not comprehending the quantitative material necessary to be literate in chemistry. In one important area known as chemical equilibrium, it was common for several students to receive single-digit scores on exams. To remedy that dilemma, I instituted cooperative learning in the class to enhance the level of student engagement with the material, to provide more "instructional" opportunities than I alone could provide, and to enable me to get a better understanding of what confused individual students. Groups of three or four students are assigned the second day of class after I have gathered some background information on the first day. These groups work together throughout the entire term and are "required" to meet out of class to work on homework assignments.

In the lab, I replaced the one- and two-week experiments in my courses with semester-long, small-group (two or three students) projects. Instead of mostly analyzing white powders that were completely soluble in water, students now analyze things such as benzene and toluene from auto exhaust in air; trihalomethanes in drinking water; chloride, nitrate, nitrite, phosphate, and sulfate ions in soils and foods; the amino acid content of foods such as milk, popcorn, and beer; caffeine, theophylline, and theobromine in chocolate; polycyclic aromatic hydrocarbons in hamburgers, oysters, creosote, and diesel exhaust; heavy metals in sludges, soil, paint, and wine; and DNA restriction fragment analysis. In many ways these projects have imparted more of a research-like experience to the lab.

The use of cooperative learning in the class and lab has been an unqualified success. I no longer have students receiving single-digit scores on exams. Students' ability to understand complex, multi-step equilibria problems have noticeably improved. The atmosphere in class changed from a competitive to cooperative one. The benefit of cooperative learning in providing a supportive environment for females and minorities has been demonstrated (Treisman 1992; Seymour 1995). Members of underrepresented groups have been especially receptive to the cooperative learning environment in my courses, and student course evaluations have improved since the change. More detailed descriptions of my methods and their impact on student learning are available in *Analytical Chemistry* (Wenzel 1995, 1998).

Faculty Development Seminars on Women's Studies

IN 1992-93, I PARTICIPATED in the first of three faculty development seminars on the connection between women's studies and science. The first was funded by Bates College to help support course development for the interdisciplinary Women's Studies Program, which had been recently established. The latter two in 1997-98 and 1998-99 were part of the National Science Foundation-funded project, *Women and Scientific Literacy: Building Two-Way Streets,* sponsored by the Association of American Colleges and Universities.

One goal of these seminars was to acknowledge and understand the current practice and culture of science. In the seminars, we considered how science is often taught and conceptualized as a body of facts, and we examined the ramifications of such a conceptualization. Another goal was to examine feminist critiques of science. We explored the idea of creating a different science that not only better accommodated women and minorities, but included in its basis an acknowledgment of the gendered, "raced," and "classed" nature of scientific knowledge and its production. Both the leaders and participants hoped that the seminar would improve science courses at Bates.

Participation in the seminars has had many positive outcomes for me, besides fostering interactions with colleagues in other departments and programs at Bates. Most importantly, it caused me to examine many issues I had never before considered. Reading Sandra Harding (1994, 1991), Evelyn Fox Keller (1987, 1985), and Helen Longino and Evelynn Hammonds (1990), caused me to consider the extent to which science was influenced by culture. I began to appreciate the way in which social, political, and economic interests of a particular culture drive science, and how the benefits of science are disproportionately distributed. Reading Keller and Harding along with Sue V. Rosser and Bonnie Kelley (1994) and Ruth Hubbard (1986) enabled me to see that science, as currently practiced, is characterized by a competitive and masculine nature. I had always believed that science was objective, but, through the works of scholars like Martin Deutsch (1958), Lorraine Daston (1992), Elizabeth Fee (1981, 1982), Ann Fausto-Sterling (1976), and Ruth Bleier (1986), I found myself questioning this basic tenet, and the extent to which the idea of objectivity could be used to obscure the historical and social context of science.

Because I had instituted these changes in my upper-level courses, it was reassuring in these seminars to read and hear perspectives about the value of cooperative learning and investigative or discovery-based laboratories (Treisman 1992; Seymour 1995). I had not fully appreciated or exploited the value that cooperative learning could have in developing skills for teamwork and honing communication abilities. Cooperative learning also created a more supportive and less competitive environment, which in turn improved student retention and attitudes toward chemistry, especially with women and minorities. Still, I had not yet created female-friendly courses. I realized I could benefit from adopting a feminist pedagogy so that students could think more profoundly about science as an enterprise interwoven with society and culture. In particular, these new insights exacerbated my concerns about the methods I was using in introductory courses, since changes at that level would have a broader impact.

The New Introductory Chemistry

IN 1998, A COLLEAGUE, Rachel Austin, and I began to offer a new version of our two-semester general chemistry course. In our section, fundamental chemical topics and concepts are related to the study of the environment. The sequence fulfills the introductory chemistry pre-requisite for all upper-level chemistry courses and satisfies the chemistry requirement for Bates' BS degree. We use the same text as the other sections and provide supplementary readings to develop the environmental connections. The first semester, "Chemical Structure and its Importance in the Environment," focuses on an understanding of atomic and molecular structure and the forces that account for the different phases of matter. The second semester "Chemical Reactivity in Environmental Systems," focuses on chemical reactions and how chemists study them. I teach the first semester, which will be the focus of the following discussion.

I have established certain goals that I believe distinguish my course from other introductory chemistry courses. These goals, which are listed in the syllabus, would not have resulted without my participation in the faculty development seminars.

> GOAL 1
> To learn a significant amount of fundamental concepts of chemistry. Some of these are well established and seem almost beyond refute. Others we will have to accept on faith and a degree of skepticism is worth retaining.

> GOAL 2
> To learn that science does not know all the answers. This is especially so in the study of the environment, and many of our current understandings will be revised as further study takes place.

I use our current understanding of atomic and molecular structure as one means of showing why skepticism is appropriate. The idea that electrons have a wave-particle duality, that multi-lobed p-, d-, and f-orbitals exist, and that electrons can pass through regions of zero probability to get from one lobe to another are some features of atomic and molecular structure that are counter-intuitive and unsettling. We expect students to accept these as "facts," yet they cannot inspect these assertions first-hand. We may tell them about experimental evidence that supports these conclusions, but students rarely perform the experiments themselves. In my course we examine some of the historical milestones (the work of Thompson, Planck, Einstein, Millikan, Bohr, and Rutherford), but more importantly, we consider the ambivalence that they and others had about some of the concepts within the emerging field of quantum physics. Although the students realize that they are not in a position to develop an alternative mathematical description of atoms and molecules, they appreciate that our current picture has enough unsettling components that makes another acceptable theory possible.

It is much easier to show the limitations of our knowledge in environmental science. Having an understanding of blackbody radiation and absorption of radiant energy by molecules, students can understand the science of global warming. Once covered in class, they then read a variety of articles on global warming, several of which describe areas where uncertainty exists in our understanding. We discuss the necessity, but associated uncertainty, in the use of computer models for predicting long-term consequences of global warming. They also read an article titled "Science Has Spoken: Global Warming Is a Myth," which argues that global warming is not a significant issue (Robinson and Robinson 1997).

Faced with uncertainties and conflicting opinions, one student in obvious frustration wanted to know who was correct and just how serious an issue global warming was. Other students were struggling with this issue as well. The realization that uncertainty will always be present in scientific investigations, that well-designed experiments may add knowledge but never completely remove the uncertainty, and that science is not an infallible exercise is valuable.

The students then discuss in their small groups the question:

> What is your opinion regarding whether emissions of carbon dioxide and other greenhouse gases should be reduced?

The groups then share their views and justifications with the entire class.

They also read several articles about the possibility of adding iron to the ocean to promote phytoplankton growth. The increased growth would require more carbon dioxide, potentially mitigating global warming. Another article summarizes an actual ocean experiment in which a sizeable area of the ocean was seeded with iron. A rapid phytoplankton bloom did occur but without additional iron had diminished within a few days. Even though the scheme was not practical, students in small groups are then asked to consider a more important question: Would they support initiatives to undertake global climate engineering?

GOAL 3
To participate in and learn about the process through which scientists undertake investigations and create knowledge.

The process of science is developed in the classroom on several occasions. I have already mentioned the early historical development of quantum physics. Having used the molecules ozone, nitric oxide, nitrogen dioxide, and nitric acid to demonstrate the fundamentals of Lewis structures, students can understand the chemistry of stratospheric ozone-layer depletion and ozone formation in the troposphere. In particular, the history of our understanding of ozone-layer depletion is examined in detail.

We begin with James Lovelock's development of the electron capture detector, the first device that enabled people to measure the low levels of chlorofluorocarbons (CFC's or freons) in the atmosphere. Sherry Rowland's interest in the fate of CFC's in the atmosphere peaked after hearing Lovelock talk about his new instrument and observations, which included measurable levels of CFC's in the air on the western coast of Scotland (implying that they had come from the United States), and higher levels of CFC's the closer Lovelock got to the U.S. during a trip on a Westbound freighter. We examine the importance of the discovery of the Antarctic ozone hole by British workers doing balloon flights in 1985, and how the chemistry and physics that explain the formation of the hole were elucidated. Students are especially interested to learn that prior satellite data also showed the ozone hole, but scientists arbitrarily ignored data from the South Pole because the amounts were so low as to suggest a problem with the measurements. We read about the Montreal protocol, alternatives to freons, and articles that present differing views about which alternatives are preferable. The history of ozone-layer depletion shows the sometimes serendipitous nature of scientific discovery, and with the ozone hole, how human nature affects scientific investigations. Students also learn about the important role scientists can have in influencing policy decisions.

PROCESS AND INTERACTION

The best way to demonstrate the process of science, however, is to have students undertake a scientific investigation. The lab linked to the course has consisted of a semester-long, class project in which students work in small groups and examine whether acid rain mobilizes metal ions from soil and minerals, and whether plants grown in soil impacted by acid rain take up metals at higher concentrations. Each group first has to identify questions and/or variables that need to be addressed to undertake the project. The collective list includes: the chemical constituents of acid rain; whether acid rain will be fabricated or collected rainfall; what soil and minerals to use; what types of plants to grow; what type of watering schedule to follow; what kind of water to use as a control; what types of containers to use for storing solutions and growing plants; how to design a soil leaching study; what metals to test for; and how to test for particular metals. These are all excellent questions that an "expert" would ask as well.

Given a list of seeds available from a commercial supplier, each group has to pick out two species to grow. Students have to collect soil from around campus and are provided with a mineral sample. Carrying out this type of lab experience at the introductory level has had many benefits. Students are far more engaged in the lab, work extra hours without complaints, and realize that scientific investigations do not compartmentalize into neat, three-hour blocks.

In executing the project, all of the groups encounter unanticipated problems that require decision making and revisions in the experimental design. Even though we hypothesize that metal levels will increase with increasing acidity, whether the data will support this is unknown and creates a sense of uncertainty. In fact, while some data did show the expected trend, much of it was inconclusive. On the final

37

day, each lab group presents and discusses their findings. We talk about the complexity of the system, and how more controls, repetitions, and tighter limits on variables might have helped. We discuss the ambitious nature of our original question, and how it is probably unreasonable to think that only thirty to forty hours of work would produce definitive conclusions. We also discuss how some of the data might always be inconclusive due to variables beyond our control.

The independent nature of the work enables students to make choices and creates a level of empowerment that I have never observed before in an introductory lab. Access to the greenhouse, which is restricted to students undertaking projects, contributes to a sense of being special. Using sophisticated instruments such as an atomic absorption spectrophotometer, inductively coupled plasma-atomic emission spectrophotometer, and a microwave digester also provide a sense of privilege and importance to the students. Finally, the presence of inconclusive data allows us to talk about ethical issues that require a complete, rather than selective, disclosure of results.

> GOAL 4
> To learn in interaction with, rather than isolation from, other students. Most things in the "real world" are done in interaction with other people, usually as a team effort. To benefit from working with other students, even if you dislike those with whom you are working.

In addition to the small-group lab projects, a considerable amount of in-class time is spent in cooperative learning activities to develop fundamental chemical concepts and to discuss open-ended questions, as heterogeneous as possible. Groups as heterogeneous as possible are assigned on the second day of class using information gathered on the first day.

When I first instituted cooperative learning in my classes, two common criticisms in the formal student course evaluations were surprising. One can be summarized as "science knows the answers, so just tell us them." Students did not appreciate that "discovering" a concept, even if it is firmly established, could enhance their learning. Students seem to have been acculturated to a definition of science that told them all the facts they needed to know through lectures and, then, asked them to reproduce some of them on exams. I now make a point of including questions that do not have established answers, and that involve more than just memorizing factual material, as a way of challenging a view that science knows all the answers.

The second criticism can be summarized as "I learned more from other students than I did from him." This was the most frustrating of all because based on their

exam performance, the students did learn more than their predecessors had in courses with a lecture format. In fact, students acting in an instructional capacity are one
of the important purposes of cooperative learning.

I now stress throughout the term that my concern is their learning. I emphasize
that my primary role is to provide an environment that enables them to learn. There
are occasions, of course, when information is best relayed in a lecture format when
teaching chemistry (Wenzel 1999). By discussing topics, resolving their inconsistencies
in understanding, and connecting new material to prior concepts, they will learn more.
I remind them that it is a tremendous waste of resources, abilities, and insights to view
me as the sole source of knowledge. When they do well on exams, which is typical, I
praise them and stress how cooperative learning is enabling them to learn more than
they would in a lecture format. At times I feel like a "spin doctor," but since science
students seem so conditioned to seeing the instructor as the source of knowledge and
science as knowing the answers, they need to be constantly reminded otherwise.

> GOAL 5
> To appreciate that science occurs in a social context. To explain a little bit of
> what I mean by this, think about your response to the following:
>
> Do you trust the scientist who concludes that second-hand smoke is not haz-
> ardous to your health when you learn that the person's research was funded by
> R. J. Reynolds?
>
> Similarly, do you trust the scientist who concludes the opposite when you learn
> that both of the person's parents were smokers who died of lung cancer at a rel-
> atively young age and that the research was funded by the organization Citizens
> Against Smoking?

This goal is addressed in the classroom and lab. For example, when given a list of
commercially available seeds, students pick common items like tomatoes, beans, and
grass to grow. Rice is not an option, and I use this as an occasion to discuss how our
choices might change if we lived in a different part of the world. After the unit on
atmospheric chemistry, students are asked within their groups to consider the following situation:

> Two options exist for significant reductions of NO_x emissions. One is to man-
> date reductions on emissions from approximately 30 power plants in the
> Midwest. The other is to mandate improved emission devices on new cars sold
> in the Midwest and East. These devices would add about $1,000 to the cost of

each new car. Each option provides about the same overall amount of reduction in NO_x emissions, and the reductions achieved by one of the options are generally regarded as representing a sufficient level of NO_x reduction under current conditions that exist in the environment. As head of the Environmental Protection Agency, which option would you select? Defend your selection.

During the ensuing class discussion, I have literally had shouting matches involving both women and men about whether a car was a necessity, arguing that raising the cost was unfair to lower-income people. This leads to a discussion about how a person's economic status might influence his/her decision making.

In another example, students are asked in their groups to consider the following, "Should developing countries have to participate in greenhouse-gas, emission-reduction programs?" Implicit in an affirmative answer is the realization that developing countries would be required to use more energy efficient, but expensive technology, whereas the United States was able to use cheaper, dirtier technology during its development. While American students are generally more comfortable in saying that developing countries ought to use more costly technology, international students usually do not agree with such a view.

For example, this past year I had four international students in the course, two from Kenya, one from Ethiopia, and one from Thailand. All four were quite adamant that it was unfair to put such restriction on their countries. Pointing out the disparity in wealth between their countries and the United States, they were critical of the fact that the United States, with its wealth, had yet to make meaningful attempts to curtail carbon dioxide emissions. They felt it was hypocritical that we should expect their countries to possibly suppress growth and development by making sacrifices our country was unwilling to make.

The small-group format, with subsequent reporting-out to the entire class, helps bring forth such views. I doubt these students would have spoken up to the entire class, outnumbered as they were by more than ten-to-one. I also make sure that the students realize that the views being expressed are in part of product of our social and our cultural backgrounds, and that our background often influences our decision making in policy matters and scientific endeavors.

Several class periods are also devoted to nuclear chemistry, a topic that is often omitted from general chemistry courses because of time constraints. Given the controversy over nuclear power, nuclear weapons, and nuclear waste disposal, it is an area of particular relevance to students. Furthermore, I have students read a chapter titled "Women in Radioactivity" from a recently published book *Women in Chemistry*. The decision to include this reading was inspired by the readings in the

Women and Scientific Literacy seminars, which included Rosser and Kelly (1994), Rayner-Canham and Rayer-Canham (1998), Hammonds (1986), and Sandler, Silverberg, and Hall (1996). The field of nuclear chemistry had a disproportionately large number of women in its early years, and we examine what promoted such participation (e.g., primarily the interdisciplinary nature of the field and a handful of mentors who welcomed women in their labs). We also examine the barriers these women had to overcome in getting an education and furthering their career.

The nuclear chemistry unit occurred at the end of the term the first time I taught the course. When I asked the students' general response to the reading, the very last of the course, I literally had a chorus from the women that it was the best thing we had read all term. Many men expressed a similar sentiment. The next year, I moved the unit to an earlier point in the term to ensure that we had proper time to discuss the reading. Also, given the overwhelming interest expressed by students and my own growing confidence after participating in the three faculty-development seminars, I taught a new course "Women in Chemistry" in the Winter term of 2000, now to be offered every other year.

While not a major emphasis, I also want to start developing the student's ability to make persuasive arguments in writing. For example, students were asked to write an essay to a presidential candidate explaining why, if elected, she or he ought to support the Kyoto Treaty to reduce greenhouse gases. I intend to expand the number of such writing assignments in future installments of the course.

Lastly, it is worth considering whether science occupies a privileged position in environmental policy making that it might not deserve. Given the uncertainties that exist in predicting the long-term consequences of global warming and the likelihood that these will never be completely resolved, we can ask whether scientific contributions then begin to confuse the issue. Given that carbon dioxide levels are increasing because of higher use of fossil fuel (something accepted by everyone but the staunchest opponents of global warming), we can ask whether it is a given that consequences must result, obliging us is to reduce emissions irrespective of whether we understand all the consequences. Students are asked to consider this in their small groups, and then we discuss their thoughts as an entire class.

Response from students to the course has been overwhelmingly positive. They appreciate the format of the lab. They have even asked that I incorporate more cooperative learning into the class (currently a 50:50 mix of lecture and cooperative learning). They appreciate the environmental connection, the discussion of open-ended questions, and the social contextualization of science. Those going on to upper-level chemistry courses say that they are well prepared.

Some upper-level chemistry and biochemistry majors who have not taken the course believe the course is easier because it emphasizes the development of a broader skill set and connects material to the environment. Students who have taken the course, however, do not agree. Several students a year have had to switch to a traditional section for the second semester because of scheduling constraints. They have not reported any deficiencies that inhibit their performance.

Future Developments

IT IS IMPOSSIBLE FOR me to imagine the course ever becoming static, but there are several areas where more significant and immediate changes are needed. One is structuring more classroom time for cooperative learning activities. I had originally intended most of the course to involve cooperative learning, but cut back after my first experience with it at the introductory level. Since cooperative learning has gone well in the thematic course, and students have asked for more of it, expansion is warranted.

I also hope to further develop historical, social, and cultural aspects of material in the course. Several of the authors we read in our seminars contend that it is not enough simply to make courses female-friendly through the development of cooperative and investigative learning activities. They argue the importance of also examining the gendered, raced, and classed character of scientific knowledge and its production (Harding 1994; Harding 1991; Keller 1987; Keller 1985; Rosser and Kelley 1994; Fausto-Sterling 1990). I have begun to move in this direction, but have much further to go. There are many general chemistry topics about which I have no historical knowledge. Researching some of these is bound to provide insights that will enliven the material and illuminate the process of scientific inquiry and discovery.

The lab will change considerably with some newly acquired equipment. There will still be a semester-long project, although it will be scaled back in scope. Students will examine whether plants grown in soil that contains leaded paint dust absorb more lead, and whether the concentration of lead in the plant depends on the acidity of the rainwater. The final report will involve an in-class oral presentation and a written report in the form of a journal article. Several shorter projects will be undertaken as well. Rainfall will be collected and analyzed for nitric and sulfuric acid using ion chromatography to see whether the student's watering solutions are reasonable representations of rain in our area. A gas chromatograph-mass spectrometer will be used to examine volatile chemicals in car exhaust and volatile emissions from evergreen trees. Air will then be collected around Lewiston, Maine for evidence of each of these sources. Shorter written reports will be required for these experiments as a way of giving the students more writing experience and feedback for the semester-long project report.

Lastly, it is essential that I develop formative and summative assessment methods for the broader skill set emphasized in the course. Currently, these are assessed in only a summative way under the category "participation." Class and lab participation grades are assigned on the basis of my own personal observations and assessment. Formalized procedures to assess how well students are working within groups, contributing to discussions, participating in experimental design and execution are needed. I plan to experiment with some methods described in an excellent book on assessment (Angelo and Cross 1993).

Conclusion

MY PARTICIPATION IN FACULTY development seminars relating women's studies to science lent further support for the new teaching methods I had incorporated in my upper-level courses. More importantly, I gained a broader perspective on what ought to be taught in chemistry courses and became convinced that I had to change how I taught introductory chemistry. I now believe it is essential that students in an introductory chemistry course conduct real scientific investigations, work extensively in cooperative group settings, appreciate some of the limitations of science, examine open-ended questions that do not have established answers, and consider science in a social and cultural context.

Many papers we read during the seminars comment on examples or practices within the fields of biology, physics, and mathematics. However, inclusion of material related to chemistry was rare. Anne Fausto-Sterling advocates the importance of including aspects of the historical and cultural context of science in an undergraduate curriculum and provides examples of books that would support such an approach in biology, physics, mathematics, and engineering. She does not provide an example for chemistry, which is sorely needed.

I now find that teaching is much harder than when I started. Thinking seriously about what I want students to learn and assessing whether they are learning it is more difficult than simply planning how best to cover material. Broadening the skill and knowledge set beyond content and lab techniques has created new challenges in facilitating student learning, which have provided an invigorating lift at a time in my career when teaching might have become boring. Given the nature of these challenges, it seems doubtful that teaching could ever become routine. For that, I am most grateful.

Acknowledgments

I WOULD LIKE TO thank the *Women and Scientific Literacy* team, Pam Baker, Sharon Kinsman, Georgia Nigro, Bonnie Shulman, and Elizabeth Tobin, for their role in organizing and facilitating the National Science Foundation-funded faculty development seminars. I am indebted to Rachel Austin for her mutual interest in developing an environmentally based general chemistry course and for the boundless enthusiasm she has brought to the task. Finally, the support of the National Science Foundation (DUE-9950314) for additional lab equipment is greatly appreciated.

Works Cited

Angelo, T.A., and K.P. Cross. 1993. *Classroom assessment techniques: A handbook for college teachers,* 2nd Edition. San Francisco: Jossey-Bass Publishers.

Bleier, R., J.W. Leavitt, and L. Gordon. 1988. Introduction to a decade of feminist critiques in the natural sciences. *Signs,* 14: 182-184.

Bleier, R. 1986. Sex differences research: Science or belief. In R. Bleier, ed. *Feminist approaches to science.* New York: Pergamon Press, 147-164.

Daston, L. 1992. Objectivity and the escape from perspective. *Social Studies of Science,* 22: 597-618.

Deutsch, M. 1958. Evidence and inference in nuclear research. *Daedalus,* 87: 88-98.

Fausto-Sterling, A. 1990. Race, gender, and science. *Transformations,* 4-12.

____. 1976. The myth of neutrality: Race, sex and class in science. *Radical Teacher,* 19: 21-25.

Fee, E. 1982. A feminist critique of scientific objectivity. *Science for the People,* 14: 5-8, 30-33.

____. 1981. Is feminism a threat to scientific objectivity? *International J. Women's Studies,* 4: 378-92.

Hammonds, E. 1986. Never meant to survive: A black woman's journey. *Radical Teacher,* 30: 8-15.

Harding, S. 1994. Is science multicultural? Challenges, resources, opportunities, uncertainties. In D.T. Goldberg, ed. *Multiculturalism: A critical reader.* Cambridge, MA: Blackwell Publishers, 344-370.

Harding, S.G. 1991. *Whose science? Whose knowledge?: Thinking from women's lives.* Ithaca, NY: Cornell University Press.

Hubbard, R. March/April 1986. Facts and feminism: Thoughts on the masculinity of natural science. *Science for the People,* 16-20, 26.

Keller, E.F. 1987. Women scientists and feminist critics of science. *Daedalus,* 116: 77-97.

____. 1985. *Reflections on gender and science*. New Haven, CT: Yale University Press.

Longino, H., and E. Hammonds. 1990. Conflicts and tensions in the feminist study of gender and science. In M. Hirsch and E.F. Keller, eds. *Conflicts in feminism*, 176-183.

Rayner-Canham, M., and G. Rayner-Canham. 1998. *Women in chemistry: Their changing roles from alchemical times to the mid-twentieth century*. American Chemical Society and Chemical Heritage Foundation, 93-134.

Robinson, A.B., and Z.W. Robinson. Dec. 4 1997. Science has spoken: Global warming is a myth. *The Wall Street Journal*.

Rosser, S.V., and B. Kelley. 1994. Introduction and phase model. *Educating women for success in science and mathematics*. Columbia, SC: U. South Carolina.

Sandler, B.R., L.A. Silverberg, and R.M. Hall. 1996. *The chilly classroom climate: A guide to improve the education of women*. Washington, DC: National Association for Women in Education.

Seymour, E. 1995. Guest comment: Why undergraduates leave the sciences. *Amer. J. Physics*, 63: 199-202:

Treisman, U. 1992. Studying students studying calculus: A look at the lives of minority students in college. *The College Mathematics Journal*, 23: 362-372.

Wenzel, T. J. 1999. The lecture as a learning device. *Analytical Chemistry*, 4: 817A-819A.

____. 1998. Cooperative group learning in undergraduate analytical chemistry. *Analytical Chemistry*, 70: 790A-795A.

____. 1995. A new approach to undergraduate analytical chemistry. Analytical Chemistry, 67: 470A-475A.

Integrating Science into Gender and Women's Studies Programs

Katrin Schultheiss

The world, we hardly need to remind ourselves, is shaped ever more obviously and ever more directly by science and technology. Access to and control over science and technology, whether at the level of the individual citizen, the community, or the nation, is probably the single greatest determinant of political power. The vast majority of today's students enter college fully cognizant of this reality. Many are far more computer literate than their instructors; most regard scientific advances such as cloning and the mapping of the human genome as inevitable and unproblematic. Ironically, however, the very omnipresence of science in students' lives today has rendered it largely invisible. It has, in a sense, become the very air they breathe.

Curiously—or perhaps alarmingly—colleges and universities have done little to encourage critical thinking about scientific and technological "progress." Indeed, if my own institution is at all a guide, universities have touted the wondrous benefits of "distance learning" and "smart classrooms" as if solving the crisis in American education were only a matter of upgrading computer equipment and finding a good internet service provider.

Gender and women's studies programs, though rarely guilty of mindless techno-boosterism, have only recently begun to take on science as a legitimate realm of critical inquiry. With the exception of the small number of scholars engaged in feminist science studies (many of whom are based in science or sometimes social science departments), gender and women's studies programs have maintained their distance from the sciences. This gap is rooted deeply in the specific historical circumstances that gave rise to women's studies as a discipline. The product of radicalism that produced both the civil rights movements and the women's liberation movement in the 1960s, the first women's studies programs were founded by campus activists as the academic arm of the feminist movement. They were designed to fill glaring gaps in an androcentric curriculum, to promote feminist theory as a legitimate form of intellectual inquiry, and to provide a sort of intellectual, political, and emotional home for women in a heavily male-dominated environment. In that particular context, science was widely regarded by feminist scholars as a masculine preserve, a characterization frequently born out by self-consciously all-male science faculties. Although there were always acknowledged individual exceptions to the male scientist (people like Rachel Carson, Jane Goodall, or Marie Curie), they were usually understood to be just that, exceptions. Women's studies tended to be dominated by students and faculty in the humanities, especially literature, and to a lesser extent, the social sciences.

This tradition continues today. While many of us have learned to teach across disciplines, we rarely cross over into the natural or "hard" sciences. This is partially the result of the widespread perception that while supposedly any intelligent person can learn enough history, literature, or sociology to teach basic concepts, science is the realm of the specialist. It is "too hard." While non-scientist feminist scholars are often guilty of upholding this perception, it is also consciously or unconsciously supported by scientists themselves who promote the image of science as beyond the grasp of non-scientists. Even as many women's studies programs broaden their scope of inquiry to include masculinity, sexuality, non-western feminisms, and the myriad dimensions of gender construction, courses that include science and technology remain a rarity. While growing numbers of programs are making interdisciplinarity the sine qua non of gender and women's studies curricula, the mandate to cross disciplinary boundaries too often fails to include the sciences.

This disciplinary separation is strengthened by the stereotype, often unwittingly upheld by women's studies programs even today, that girls can't do math and science. While no one in a women's studies program would ever state this or even consciously think this, the fact that few scientists teach in women's studies programs and that as a result, science rarely appears in women's studies curricula inadvertently lends credence to this stereotype. Despite the well-intentioned efforts of high school and college teachers and counselors, students in women's studies courses today too often still subscribe to this idea. In the Gender and Women's Studies Program at my own institution, for example, almost all of our minors (the only status we offer) continue to major in the humanities or social sciences. Women's studies courses that avoid all discussion of science serve to reinforce students' belief that women have nothing to do with science.

In recent years, some progress has been made in bridging the gender gap in the sciences. Considerable effort has been exerted to get girls and women to take and excel in science and math courses and to choose careers in the sciences. At the same time, the field of "science studies" has made science a legitimate site of feminist inquiry. Over the course of the last decade or so, a growing number of feminist scientists have made questions about the social, political, and ethical implications of scientific research central to their own research and teaching; they are looking critically at research methodologies, professional protocols, career paths, and pedagogies provoking further questions and raising not a few hackles within the more conventional scientific community (Barad 1998; Harding 1986; AAC&U 1999).

Yet, in some ways—and in direct contradiction to the intentions of its practitioners—feminist science studies has served to broaden the perceived distance between women's studies and the sciences. Many scientists not familiar with the subtleties of the gender and science debates in science studies maintain that "feminists" are questioning the whole notion of objectivity and are attempting to convince people that science is no more valid than any other set of subjective beliefs. They accuse "feminists" of being hostile to science in general, forgetting that many of the most influential feminist science critics are practicing scientists themselves. Because very few scientists are actually part of women's studies programs, many scientists in science departments perceive critical science studies to be an attack on their disciplines. Thus, many science departments actively or passively discourage their students from pursuing women's studies or taking feminist science studies classes, while women's studies faculty often steer clear of science entirely to avoid being seen as "anti-science."

Bridging the Divide

IF THE CHASM BETWEEN women's studies and the sciences is ever to be bridged, several steps need to be taken. First, gender and women's studies programs need to recruit and integrate faculty members trained in the sciences. This will be very difficult for a number of reasons. Young scientists, who are the most likely to be interested in gender and women's studies, usually cannot risk their professional reputation by becoming involved in women's studies programs. Science departments often do not regard women's studies courses as "real science" and many see a young scientist's interest in women's studies as evidence that s/he is not "serious" about science. Young scientists rightly fear not getting tenure in their home science departments. Practically speaking, then, the most likely candidates for recruitment would be tenured scientists.

Links between women's studies and science departments could also be forged on a less formal basis. Perhaps the only way to start would be to get a tenured scientist from a science department to teach and work with women's studies. This could then lead to further links and stronger professional connections. Once they see a respected member of their home department teaching in a women's studies program, science students might be more inclined to take women's studies courses.

Another way to build these connections is for women's studies faculty to team teach with science faculty (see Tahamont, Brown, and Lindman and Ginorio and Olmstead in this volume). Again, the challenge here is to gain approval from science departments to count such courses as "real science." A number of universities have instituted courses like these. The Honors College, for example, at the University of Illinois at Chicago emphasizes team teaching across disciplines. Women's studies needs to support more team-teaching of this sort again with the aim of building ties to science departments. Team teaching also addresses the perceived problem of "expertise." With a credentialed scientist in the room, the problem of legitimacy can be solved, and instructors and students alike gain.

Finally, women's studies faculty members must be encouraged to integrate science into their introductory and theoretical courses. They need to demystify science for themselves by recognizing that much of the scientific literature *is* readable. Perhaps even more importantly, non-scientifically trained women's studies faculty must recognize that they can make an important contribution to students' understanding of science not in spite of their lack of scientific training, but because of their familiarity with feminist theory and the various intellectual contexts provided by their own disciplinary expertise.

Revising a Syllabus

IT IS WITH THIS last goal in mind that I, an historian by training, set out to revise my own syllabus for "Women's Studies 101: American Women's Experience." The impetus to create a science unit emerged directly out of my involvement in the AAC&U project, *Women and Scientific Literacy: Building Two Way Streets,* funded by the National Science Foundation. Over the course of several months of discussion with my colleagues at UIC and other institutions involved in the AAC&U initiative, I recognized how important it is to integrate science into introductory women's studies courses rather than confine it to specialized courses on topics like women's health, which are already well established in many women's studies programs. Seeking a topic that would fit easily into my overarching course theme of the role of gender in American society, I developed a two-week unit that examines the science of establishing gender difference in the past and present.

At the most basic level, my goal in this unit is to demystify science for non-science students and raise new questions in the minds of science students (of whom we always have a few). More specifically, I aim not only to teach the students something about how scientists have explored and are still exploring the differences between the sexes but to get them to understand that science is not—and has not ever been—value-free. In no sense do I strive to undermine the value of scientific knowledge; to the contrary, I hope to instill in students a willingness to subject science to the same tests of critical reasoning that they have learned to apply in other disciplines.

I usually begin with a lecture/discussion that provides some historical background to the question of gender difference. Students get a good laugh from ancient Greek explanations of gender formation as the product of humoral balance and are generally incredulous when told that many nineteenth-century physicians insisted that higher education caused infertility in women by diverting blood away from the reproductive organs to the brain. Yet these now preposterous-sounding beliefs serve to prompt students to ask what presuppositions have gone into current theories of men and women's supposedly different inherent aptitudes and proclivities. Carol Tavris' *The Mismeasure of Woman* (1992) offers a very accessible, often entertaining evaluation of the current fascination with establishing gender differences in the brain. Alternatively, or sometimes additionally, Anne Fausto-Sterling's *Myths of Gender* (1985) provides a devastating critique of the actual methodologies employed by scientists intent on proving that gender difference is biologically determined. She successfully demonstrates that, like their nineteenth-century predecessors, modern scientists often sacrifice good science for political purposes. While more difficult for non-science students to read, Fausto-Sterling's book has the advantages of having been written by a practicing scientist and, as a result, of engaging more deeply with actual science. Whereas Tavris's work is about science, Fausto-Sterling's work *is* science.

Finally, I frequently assign Ruth Hubbard's classic article (1990), "Have Only Men Evolved?" which exposes the sexist biases that lie at the root of Darwin's theories of human evolution and crucially shape the work of modern evolutionary biologists and animal behaviorists. Most importantly, she shows that Darwin's biases reflect the cultural beliefs of the society in which he lived and are not merely the prejudices of a single individual. Like Fausto-Sterling, Hubbard's goal is not simply to reveal hidden unfairness masquerading as scientific truth, but to demonstrate that sexist presumptions have often tainted the very conclusions drawn by some of the world's most influential scientists.

These readings become the basis for a wide-ranging discussion in which I ask students a number of open-ended questions: For example, what are the questions in scientists' minds that are driving their research? Where did those questions come from? What criteria are used for determining the significance of experimental results? Who determines which studies are worth funding? On what basis? Does the identity of the scientist (class, race, gender, religion, political convictions, etc.) matter in shaping the research agenda that is carried out? On the whole, I would say that this unit has been successful in getting students to think critically about science and how it is produced, practiced, and implemented. Its weaknesses are largely the product of having to cram many new concepts and much unfamiliar material into a very short period of time. These problems are probably insurmountable at the introductory level.

Upper-Level Course

MY OTHER EFFORTS TO integrate science into women's studies courses have occurred in upper-level courses on women's health. Because I am a trained historian, my first course on the topic centered almost exclusively on the social and cultural history of women's health care. There was little, if any, science or traditional history of science and medicine involved. Still, I posed questions about the role of science in society and the establishment of scientific authority. I also tried to get students to understand that the production and dissemination of medical/scientific knowledge is a political process involving the negotiation of power and the contestation of authority, as well as an intellectual process of scientific discovery. For example, we studied the history of childbirth from colonial times to the present emphasizing themes such as the rise of the medical professions, the conflicts between midwives and obstetricians, and the struggle for maternal control over the birth process. Using Judith Walzer Leavitt's excellent book, *Brought to Bed: Childbirth in America, 1750-1950* (1986), we saw that the introduction of anesthesia into the birthing room in the mid-nineteenth century was something that women demanded; many male physicians resisted anesthesia because they were unsure about how it worked and feared its potential effects on the newborn child. The spur to develop effective painkillers came in large part from clients—that is women— and not primarily from male doctors. The process of introducing these substances into the birthing room became a matter of negotiating power between the birthing mother, the obstetrician or attending physician, and in many cases, a midwife and other women attending the birth.

Anthropologist Emily Martin's *The Woman in the Body* (1987) offers an instructive counterpoint to Leavitt's book, showing how current metaphors of birth as a mechanical process construct the baby as the product and the uterus as the producing machine, thereby rendering women bystanders in their own birthing experience. In this book and in her classic article "The Egg and the Sperm: How Science Has Constructed a Romance Based on Stereotypical Male-Female Roles" (1991), Martin effectively demonstrates that culturally produced metaphors and assumptions about gender often shape the way doctors and other scientists (as well as birthing mothers) think about and teach childbirth and many other biological processes (1991).

More recently, I offered a revised version of this course that looks at women's health in a multidisciplinary context. Designed for upper-level undergraduates and graduate students in the health and allied health fields and students in other disciplines interested in health topics, the class examines such issues as menstruation, menopause, abortion, childlessness, breast cancer, eating disorders, and depression drawing on material from the fields of history, sociology, anthropology, biology, psychology and philosophy. Through courses like "The History of Women's Health" and "Women's Health Issues," I hope that students—both those in the health fields and those who are not—come to see that the production and implementation of medical knowledge can and should be understood as, among other things, a political and cultural process subject to constant negotiation, rather than as the inevitable forward march of disembodied knowledge.

Despite the success of these courses and the importance of their contributions in and of themselves, I would not say that I have really integrated "science" per se into women's studies. We do not actually study biology in these courses—aside from popular accounts of women's biology like Natalie Angier's *Woman: An Intimate Geography* (1999). Much less have I introduced any other branch of science aside from biology. While I would ideally like to do so, I do not see that I can nor do I think I necessarily should. That task can and should be left to trained scientists working, it is to be hoped, in conjunction with gender and women's studies programs. I can, however, teach students some new ways of thinking about science and get them to see that science exists in a social, cultural, and political context. In doing so, I and my students alike can begin to see science as a critical and scrutable part of the world in which we live.

There is a great emphasis these days in gender and women's studies programs on rethinking and revising what it is that gender and women's studies programs should be teaching. Faculty are retooling and revamping their syllabi and holding workshops to educate themselves about the latest developments in the field. Many institutions have made gay and lesbian studies an integral part of their programs; they are "internationalizing" their curricula by stressing connections between women's lives in the United States and women's lives throughout the world, as they put Western concepts of gender into a world context. A similar effort needs to be made to encourage women's studies faculty to rethink the role of science in a feminist curriculum in general and in their own courses in particular. If gender and women's studies is truly the interdisciplinary field it claims to be, then it can no longer ignore, even in its introductory courses, the vast realm of the sciences.

Works Cited

Angier, Natalie. 1999. *Woman: An intimate geography*. Boston: Houghton Mifflin.

Association of American Colleges & Universities. 1999. *Frequently asked questions about feminist science studies*. Washington, DC: Association of American Colleges and Universities.

Barad, Karen. 1998. Agential realism: Feminist interventions in understanding scientific practices. In Mario Biagioli, ed. *The science studies reader*. New York: Routledge, 1-11.

Fausto-Sterling, Anne. 1985. *Myths of gender: Biological theories about women and men*. New York: Basic Books.

Harding, Sandra G. 1986. *The science question in feminism*. Ithaca, NY: Cornell University Press.

Hubbard, Ruth. 1990. Have only men evolved? In *The politics of women's biology*. New Brunswick, NJ: Rutgers University Press.

Leavitt, Judith Walzer. 1986. *Brought to bed: Childbearing in America (1750-1950)*. New York: Oxford University Press.

Martin, Emily. 1987. *The woman in the body*. Boston: Beacon Press.

____. 1991. The Egg and the sperm: How science has constructed a romance based on stereotypical male-female roles. *Signs* 16: 485-501.

Rosser, Sue V., ed. 1995. *Teaching the majority: Breaking the gender barrier in science, mathematics, and engineering*. New York: Teachers College Press.

Tavris, Carol. 1992. *The mismeasure of woman*. New York: Simon and Schuster.

Issues in Women's Health: An Interdisciplinary Experience

Maria Tahamont, Janet Moore Lindman, and Virginia Brown

Introduction

This article describes the development of a new course, "Issues in Women's Health," which emerged from our participation in the Association of American Colleges and Universities' (AAC&U) *Women and Scientific Literacy* project, funded by the National Science Foundation. The intellectual framework for this course comes out of our educational training, our participation in faculty development seminars sponsored by the project, and our individual experiences as teachers and feminists who ascribe to values of progressive and empowering pedagogy.[1]

Our participation in AAC&U's grant has informed our intellectual approaches to transdisciplinary curriculum development. As members of a faculty research seminar that we helped to create for this project, we read and discussed a variety of works relevant to the grant topic from the fields of science studies, feminist philosophy, and pedagogy. We gleaned new insights about the lack of parity for women and minorities in the sciences, mathematics, and engineering and learned about ways to create more "female friendly" science courses. We became aware of the "seemingly" non-existent relationship between faculty in the arts, humanities, and the social sciences with those in the "hard" sciences generally, and on our campus specifically.[2] In designing this course, we built upon the knowledge gained and the alliances formed in the seminar to bring women's studies and the sciences into a more productive curricular relationship at our institution. At the same time, we wished to provide our students with a positive experience in an interdisciplinary course that presented "science in context" (Harding 1993).

At a much broader level, as educators we wanted to address the question of how to overcome the dilemma of living in "a world in which science seems an illegitimate place for women, and gender studies seems an inappropriate enterprise for scientists" (Fausto-Sterling 1992, 337). By initiating a conversation among faculty in various disciplines and designing a course specifically on the topic of women's health, we wanted to encourage further professional interactions across departments and to expand the range of interdisciplinary education available at our university. Further, we agree with Anne Fausto-Sterling (337) that "science needs feminism and feminism needs science," both for the rigor and vitality of our respective fields and for the future status and opportunity of women and minorities in American society.

Setting Learning Goals for an Interdisciplinary Course

OUR GOAL IN CREATING this course was to join women's studies and the biological sciences together by placing physiology in the social, historical, and cultural contexts of women's health issues and health care experiences. We wished to convey to our students a definition of science that captures its complexity as a product of human initiative and imagination combined with its potent cultural meaning and significant political power. As Anne Fausto-Sterling (347) defines it: "Science is a social construct, made by human beings within a particular cultural milieu."

To elucidate the ways in which "science is a contestable text, and a power field," we wanted to make explicit the societal influences upon women's health and the ways in which medical research and public policy have been traditionally crafted (Haraway 1991, 185). In addition, we examined how women's health and medical treatment have been experienced and understood within a paradigm that all too often uses the white male body as its norm. Placing biology within a cultural and historical context, we explored normal physiology and pathophysiology of women's bodies. In deliberately choosing the fields of biology and medicine—fields traditionally seen as fact-based and objective—we planned for students to speculate about how issues in women's health have been defined and promulgated within American society. By critically analyzing the information delivered to them by so-called "experts" (doctors, health care workers, biological researchers, etc.), students would realize how biases and positionality affect what is gathered, reported on, and conveyed to them by health care professionals.

The course was offered as part of the Honors Concentration and was cross-listed in the women's studies program. It met a general education requirement in the social/behavioral science bank or the science/math bank. This arrangement was a unique event at Rowan University because the course satisfied requirements in two different banks. In order to enroll, students had to have completed their basic writing courses. The actual class consisted of twenty students from a wide range of majors, including biology, psychology, communications, education, English, and history. As the professors, we represented three different academic fields: social psychology, history, and biology.

The specific objectives of this interdisciplinary course were to examine women's health issues in their social, cultural, and historical contexts; to understand the biology underlying women's health and illness and the methods used by the scientific research community to study women's health; and to analyze the gendered assumptions made in regard to women's health.

No traditional textbook was required for the course, but instead a variety of sources were used to provide students with readings that presented the social, historical, or cultural contexts of important medical issues. For example, among the articles on the topic of childbirth, we included Laurel Thatcher Ulrich's "The Living Mother of a Living Child: Midwifery and Mortality in Post Revolutionary New England"; Judith Walzer Leavitt's "Birthing and Anesthesia: The Debate Over Twilight Sleep"; and Rima Apple's "Constructing Mothers: Scientific Motherhood in the 19th and 20th Centuries."

Apple's article prompted one student to write:

> Apple had me thinking explosively and agreeing with her repeatedly. Apple discussed how motherhood had become a scientific process in the 19th and 20th centuries. The customary belief was that womanhood equated with motherhood and in this expected role, women were taught to ask doctors about mothering. These esteemed doctors were males who may not even have experienced fatherhood. How was it that they knew better? The comparison narrows down to a science/technology vs. nature dilemma. (JR, Feb. 28, 2000)

From the two weeks spent studying body image, some of the articles analyzed, including Susan Bordo's theoretical works, "The Body and the Reproduction of Femininity" and "Reading the Slender Body"; Susie Orbach's classic study, "Fat is a Feminist Issue"; and Sara Hare's article "You're Not Fat, You're Living in the Wrong Country" offered students comparative and cultural analyses of the normative expectations and demands placed on women haunted by the "ideal" female body. Agreeing with the thesis presented by Orbach, one student commented:

> The common belief in our society is that we must try as hard as we can to be
> thin and beautiful, and that there is something wrong with those who do not fit
> the ideal mold or don't seem to be making the effort. At one time I could never
> think of my weight as something to be desired by anyone, yet Orbach's article
> has an interesting point when she writes that fat can actually make a woman feel
> more secure around men by making her seem desexualized or powerful. (JF,
> Feb. 16, 2000)

One component of the course was to present the biology of women's health and
illness. It included the examination of the natural process of menstruation. The ovar-
ian, hormonal, and uterine cycles and the anatomy of the female reproductive tract
were reviewed. We scrutinized the ways in which menstruation has been medicalized
and mythologized as a disease and how the normal events associated with it have
been made into a *syndrome*. It was imperative for the students to recognize the fine
line that exists between definitions of normal/abnormal and health/illness, particularly in regard to women and their bodies. Two readings that cogently demonstrate
this issue were "Misdiagnosing the Body," from Carol Tavris' *The Mismeasure of
Woman,* and "Suckers and Horns: The Prodigal Uterus," from Natalie Angier's
book, *Woman: An Intimate Geography.*

A third component was to investigate how medical practice evolved in the context of cultural perceptions of women's traditional role in society. Typically, the
methodologies used by the scientific community have overlooked the health concerns of women or have utilized medical models developed for white male patients
that have excluded women—particularly minority women—from clinical research
trials. Diane Hales's "What Doctors Don't Know About Women's Bodies," and
Jocelyn White and Wendy Levinson's, "Primary Care of Lesbian Patients," both
illustrate the ways in which the health care system overlooks the medical concerns of
female patients generally, a problem further compounded by variables of race, class,
and sexual orientation. Similarly, this bias is evident in the invisibility of women in
early scientific research on AIDS. The article by Kathryn Anastos and Carola Marte,
"Women—The Missing Persons in the AIDS Epidemic," illustrates how the definition of the disease was formulated. This reading sparked a series of critical questions
by one student in her journal:

> According to Kathryn Anastos and Carola Marte, all too often, the researchers
> who study HIV and AIDS fail to acknowledge, or even adequately study the dif-
> ferences between those symptoms and/or conditions experienced by men and

by women with AIDS. This is most likely the result of their perception that AIDS and HIV primarily affect men, and the fact that often, research is driven by funding and not by fundamental questions. However, this brings up a very important question. How can women become aware of AIDS/HIV in reference to their own bodies when so little accurate information about the effects and symptoms of the virus on women's physiology is readily available? (CB, March 11, 2000)

As with any course, particularly a women's studies course, we encouraged the students to make connections between the course content and the larger society. Specifically, we wanted to raise their consciousness of women's status and gender roles in society, generally, and relative to women's health, specifically. This course offered the students a unique opportunity to understand biological processes in their social and political contexts. In addition, cultural biases associated with women's health and illnesses were studied within a scientific framework. One student expressed her thoughts in a journal entry on the value of learning science in context:

> However interesting and illuminating the discussion of eating disorders was, the truly surprising part of the reading and the class discussion and lecture was about the mechanics of nutrition and metabolism. I, like many college students, have not studied biology since tenth grade or perhaps a general education course freshman year. I had forgotten or never been taught much about the way the human body processes food. It put the last class about body image and this class about eating disorders in perspective. No matter how emotionally or culturally charged food and eating may be, it is first and foremost the fuel that our bodies need to survive. Fat is not an inherently bad thing as popular culture would have us believe, it is necessary to human survival. (AK, Feb. 16, 2000)

One of the two biology majors in the class made specific reference to the science component of the course and liked the fact that the social issues were put into a scientific context. She believed this approach would contribute to her success as a science major (CB, May 3, 2000).

Assignments and Teaching Techniques

We utilized a variety of assignments and teaching techniques to present the course materials.[3] Student requirements included weekly journal entries, three reaction papers, group projects (including oral presentations and written self-assessments), class participation (in both small and large groups), and e-mail postings and discussions. These strategies allowed for inclusion of multiple voices and learning styles. From the initial planning of this course, we made a concerted effort to avoid the dominant paradigm of teacher-as-expert and student-as-empty-receptacle. We employed a variety of teaching techniques to empower students in the classroom, to de-emphasize our authority as professors, and to create a safe, inclusive, and interactive learning community.

The course included journal writing with at least one entry every week based on the required readings and classroom discussions. Entries were to be substantive, thoughtful, and speculative responses to the readings and discussions and not just a recitation of the content of the readings or class discussions. We assessed the journals on both a quantitative and qualitative basis. Entries with length but without substance or short and sporadic, even if pithy and insightful, were factors taken into consideration when grading the journals. We read each journal and then met to discuss and agree upon an assessment of the student's writing performance.

Three reaction papers were required at regular intervals throughout the semester based on the assigned readings. The purpose of the reaction papers was to allow the students to be self-reflective with an understanding grounded in the content of the readings. In these papers, students offered critical and analytical comments on the assigned readings that deepened their knowledge of the subject matter. Students had the freedom to focus on an issue or set of issues from a variety of articles organized around a theme, such as body image. Again, all three instructors read and discussed all the papers before coming to consensus on the grades.

The two types of writing assignments allowed students who did not regularly participate in class discussions to demonstrate that they were engaged with the material and grasped the issues. They also opened another line of communication between the students and the teachers, a feature that was particularly important in a classroom with three professors from different disciplines and with different teaching/learning styles. This strategy permitted a safe place for introspection:

> This class seems like it's going to involve discussing women's health from a feminist perspective, which is what I expected. I was not expecting the class to become personal, though, and I'm not sure that I'm comfortable with the idea of bonding with my fellow female classmates. (JF, Jan. 22, 2000)

As an example of the creative expression the journal engendered, one student shared a poem she had composed in high school when writing about body image:

Adolescence

I've changed about ten times already.
There's a pile of clean clothes on the floor.
Empty hangers synchronized their swing to the unrelenting tick of the clock.
I'm running late as usual.
I put all the clothes back in the closet where they have a chance of looking good.
I practice sucking my tummy for the mirror again and again and
I smile as I almost become a decent size.
That feeling creeps into my lungs and I have to breathe again.
Disgusted, I turn away wishing for bigger breasts and a thin body
So that people will like me. (CS, Feb. 8, 2000)

We consistently used personal narrative in the class to consider relevant issues—a task we as professors also participated in with the students, making sure always to connect these personal revelations to the readings and topic for the day. For example, in the second class meeting on the topic of The Big Picture, we asked students to relate a personal experience they had had with the health care system. The encounters some of the students related clearly connected with the issues raised in the readings assigned for that day, such as: Is medicine sexist? What social indices are relevant to health care issues? What is the impact of a person's, race, ethnicity, class, gender, or sexual orientation on the quality of health care they receive? It was vital to make the link between the experiential and the theoretical in order to ground the students' stories in the readings. Throughout the course, we emphasized that giving voice to personal experience is useful in learning only when combined with context and a theoretical understanding of, in this case, issues of women's health.

Building on the qualitative methods described above, we provided students with several opportunities to analyze scientific data. In one exercise, we had the class use statistical material compiled by the U.S. Department of Labor to study the facts, myths, and challenges related to women in the U.S. welfare system. The students interpreted the data and presented the results in visual form, either tabular or graphic, in an overhead presentation. Through this exercise, students developed an understanding of the significance of quantitative data and increased their ability to manipulate "scientific" material and the ways in which it is reported. Furthermore, it revealed to them the application of scientific information in the formulation of public policy.

By employing small group discussions in every class, we encouraged every student to become a full participant in the course. Each group session was structured around specific tasks to facilitate a close textual analysis of the readings and substantive discussions of the issues. At times the students reported back orally. At other times they produced a written assessment, but always the small group results were shared with the whole class. For instance, on the topic of gendering of addictions, students in their small groups generated correlational statements linking the medical discourse of addiction to their social/cultural contexts. A representative from each group wrote their statements on the board, and then the whole class created categories to assign to each of these statements, such as race, gender, socio-economic status, age, and moral beliefs. By making these connections, students recognized the multiple factors that influence the construction of diagnoses of disease and forms of treatment.

On occasion, we employed a variation on the small group, since we were cognizant of the fact that even with small numbers some students remain silent. To ensure that every student's voice was heard, we used the fishbowl technique. This exercise began with four individuals seated in the middle of the room initiating the day's discussion with the rest of the class seated on the perimeter. Everyone had to participate in the fishbowl at some point in the activity. Only the individuals in the fishbowl could speak; someone had to leave the inner circle to allow a new person to enter and express her ideas. The discursive process did not stop until every voice had been heard.

To start the discussion each fishbowl exercise was begun with specific questions based on the assigned readings for the day. For example, when dealing with the topic of women's sexual health/sexual disease, the questions used to begin the fishbowl included: What does the language used in the discussion about the AIDS crisis tell us about American society? What does the early hysteria about the AIDS epidemic tell us about the U.S.? What does a zip code have to do with the risk of contracting HIV? During the exercise one of the professors facilitated the process, while the other two observed and took notes. After the fishbowl exercise concluded, the whole class analyzed the process, as well as the quality and utility of the discussion. In general, the students liked this exercise and appreciated the chance to hear from people who were not usually vocal in class discussions. It took more than one experience with this technique, however, to move beyond the personal and confessional to the analytical and contextual.

A further strategy employed to enrich the students' learning experience was group presentations. Students formed their own groups of two to three people and selected a topic relevant to the course and approved by the professors. After researching their topic, students gave an oral presentation, supplied a bibliography, and submitted a written self-assessment. Students were encouraged to showcase their material in creative ways, and most of them made use of a combination of handouts, overheads, and PowerPoint presentations. Each student was required to do a peer assessment of other groups' presentations.

One of the most powerful presentations concerned sexual violence against women. This group began their project by doing a skit recreating a situation in which a young woman attempts to explain away her boyfriend's abuse to a female friend—only to be interrupted by the boyfriend (an actor) as he entered the scene, ranting and raving. Concurrent with the skit, one of the group members had a stopwatch in her hand and every twelve seconds said, "Another woman has been assaulted." After the skit ended, the group took some time to connect this particular incident to the general pattern of abuse that many women suffer. The group's PowerPoint presentation had relayed information about the myths and truths of sexual abuse against lesbians, disabled women, college age students, and women of color. They also provided the class with contact numbers of community resources for those affected by domestic violence. Other group presentations included breast cancer, female genital mutilation, sexually transmitted diseases, and plastic surgery.

One of the benefits of the group projects was the prospect of students learning from their peers. As one student asserted:

> Being taught by peers is definitely worthwhile ... I enjoy listening to presentations that are given by my peers, especially when they include stories and information to personalize what they are saying. As a future teacher, I am always looking for new and interesting ways to present information, which is why I enjoyed the skit during the domestic violence presentation so much. (CS, April 19, 2000)

Teaching Across the Disciplines

AS INSTRUCTORS FROM VERY distinct fields, we faced many challenges trying to team-teach this course. We each had different teaching styles based on disciplinary training, teaching experience, and personalities. The format of this course as a seminar also presented a challenge, particularly for the biologist, who had never taught a course of this type before. Though she typically avoids the strict lecture format, she realized she could learn more about how to be a guide in classroom discussions. Team teaching with faculty who have experience with teaching seminar classes and utilizing feminist pedagogy was also helpful for all members, particularly the biologist. This is a relevant issue for faculty in the sciences; straying from the traditional format in the classroom can be especially problematic for them because of the strong disciplinary emphasis on teaching content.

To teach a class and measure student performance without "the test" as an essential assessment tool was also a challenge. The lack of testing relieved the students of the anxiety associated with note taking. As one student said, she was able to sit back, relax, and absorb the material and, in the process, learn much more (LS, May 3, 2000).

Teaching without a standard textbook was a novel experience for the biologist and psychologist in terms of not having a unified narrative to serve as a guidepost for the course topics. The students, on the other hand, thought this was a definite plus. As one student remarked, "I enjoyed having a diversity in the readings *much* rather than having a textbook." Another student commented that she liked not having a textbook because it allowed for a wide variety of readings in terms of time periods and authors (KB, May 3, 2000).

Of concern for all of the professors was the issue of authority in the classroom. Though one typically decenters power in a course that employs feminist pedagogy, we were more acutely aware of this when giving up power to each other. According to one student, this dynamic worked well. She liked that there was no one authority in the classroom; group work gave the students a voice in class discussions. We had to come to terms with not always having to be experts on all subjects discussed in class; that meant reacquainting ourselves with the role of learners. One student pointed out that she had the feeling the teachers were learning right along with the students (KB and LS, May 3, 2000). At the same time, we had to learn how to share "airtime" in the classroom, how not to interrupt one another or repeat the same comments or instructions. Because there were three voices of "authority" in the classroom, we had to be conscious of how much we talked. Each of us had to be wary of dominating the conversation, and we wanted to be courteous—but also comfortable—in voicing alternative points of view.

Team teaching any course involves a significant amount of time. This course was no different. The team met two to five hours a week to prepare for the class and assess the students' work. These sessions included negotiating and formulating a lesson plan for a particular class and evaluating and grading student assignments. Because we had agreed beforehand that we would all read and grade all course work, reaching an agreement in grading was critical. We willingly made a personal time commitment that went beyond the time accounted for by credit load.

Because of our dedication to the goals of the AAC&U project and our collegial relationship, we were able to become an effective and efficient team of teachers. In the course evaluations, several students affirmed this success: "Perhaps the best aspect of this course was that all three professors seemed to really enjoy team teaching. When teachers enjoy teaching, there is more effective and lasting learning." Another student wrote, "The team teaching for this course was excellent! It was a great experience for me, as a student, to be surrounded by so much unique and in-depth knowledge and expertise on so many different aspects of women's health." Students also valued the range of faculty specialties: "[Team teaching] was a neat experience. I liked having three professors who are all skilled in different subjects and who can offer a variety of perspectives on a topic" (Student evaluations, May 3, 2000).

For bridging the disciplinary divide, we had the advantage of having been part of the AAC&U grant team. The research seminar we participated in was extremely helpful to us in evaluating the construction of our own disciplinary knowledge bases and our biases about other disciplines. This self-examination led to fruitful discussions and laid the groundwork for developing this course. In designing the course, we also deepened our understanding of how to place science in historical, social, and cultural contexts. Coming from different disciplines did not, in the end, prove to be a problem. We cannot emphasize enough the benefit of working together on this grant beforehand, which prepared us with a common knowledge base and teaching strategies to work as a successful team.

Developing this course had a number of positive outcomes professionally. We enjoyed sharing creative ideas in the design and execution of classroom activities. The experience provided us with the opportunity to learn more about each other's disciplines, not only content but also in our approaches to research methodology and scholarly discourse. In team teaching, we shared the "burden" of the classes as well as the work load and responsibility for its success. By being together in the classroom, the pleasure of teaching was amplified. Finally, the camaraderie we established as a team created an atmosphere of collegiality and intellectual enthusiasm that contributed to a successful learning community.

Conclusion

DESIGNING AND TEACHING THIS course was an extraordinary experience for us as faculty. More importantly, the impact of the course on the students was clearly evident in their anonymous evaluations and their individual comments during the last class meeting. As one student put it:

> I enjoyed this class highly and felt it broadened my horizons immensely. Although this was not my major, I learned new things about who I am and why I think the way I do. With the historical perspective we saw where women's rights came from and with the scientific perspective we saw a view I never would have seen in college. Thanks, this was great. (Student evaluations, May 3, 2000)

Comments by one student suggest that the learning goals we had identified for the course had been fulfilled:

Currently, I am moving toward the completion of my college career, and I can easily say this class was my favorite ever. I loved coming to class every Wednesday, and even wanted to continue class discussions outside of class...I want the rest of the world to learn what we did because it would aid in the betterment of society. A diverse array of topics were presented and explored thoroughly. The professors had a captivating style of teaching that seemed to provoke interest and stimulation throughout the class. It seemed every student felt comfortable enough to express their ideas and questions...Overall, I commend the three experts in History, Psychology and Biology. Their expertise has helped me to broaden my base of knowledge and express my passion for women and the equality movement. Thank you! (Student evaluations, May 3, 2000)

Endnotes

1 On pedagogy, see Freire 1970; hooks 1994; and Maher & Tetreault 1994. On science and feminist pedagogy, see Rosser 1990 and Middlecamp 1995.

2 See Ginorio, 1995 and AAUW 1992, for documentary evidence on the lack of parity for women and minorities in the sciences.

3 We were fortunate to be assigned a "smart classroom," meaning we had the opportunity to use a variety of media to teach course content. For example, we showed several videos to convey material under discussion ("Slim Hopes: Advertising and the Obsession with Thinness," "A Midwife's Tale," and "AIDS: The Women Speak"). We regularly used overheads, a remote distance viewer, and Power Point presentations in class.

Works Cited

American Association of University Women. 1992. *How schools have shortchanged girls*. Washington, DC: American Association of University Women.

Fausto-Sterling, Anne. Fall 1992. Building two-way streets: The case of feminism and science. *NWSA Journal,* 4: 3, 337-347.

Ginorio, Angela B. 1995. *Warming the climate for women in academic science*. Washington, DC: Association of American Colleges and Universities.

Freire, Paolo. 1970. *Pedagogy of the oppressed*. New York: Herder & Herder.

Haraway, Donna. 1991. *Simians, cyborgs, and women: The reinvention of nature*. New York: Routledge.

Harding, Sandra. Spring 1993. Forum: Feminism and science. *NWSA Journal,* 5: 1, 51.

hooks, bell. 1994. *Teaching to transgress: Education as the practice of freedom*. New York: Routledge.

Maher, Frances A. and Mary Kay Thompson Tetreault. 1994. *The feminist classroom*. New York: Basic Books.

Middlecamp, Catherine Hurt. 1995. Culturally inclusive chemistry. In Sue V. Rosser, ed. *Teaching the majority: Breaking the gender barrier in science, mathematics, and engineering*. New York: Teacher College, Columbia University.

Rosser, Sue V. 1990. Female friendly science: Applying women's studies methods and theories to attract studies to science. New York: Pergamon Press.

Policy and Pedagogy

Section A
Science, Social Policy, and Student Learning

Issues for Ethnic Minorities and Women in Science and Engineering

Angela B. Ginorio and Marjorie Olmstead

Intellectual Framework

In her presidential talk to the American Association for the Advancement of Science (AAAS), Sheila Widnall issued a call to action to all scientists "…that the feedback loop of lowered expectations based on sex or race, leading to lowered self-image and finally to lower performance, be broken by conscious action by faculty and students" (1988). Ten years later, when the proposal for the course "Issues for Ethnic Minoritiesand Women in Science and Engineering" was submitted, that call to action was still pertinent to education in the U.S. and to our own institution, the University of Washington. The proposal stated: "The statistics at the University of Washington reflect national trends with lower participation in the physical sciences and engineering of both ethnic minorities and women." The proposal called for offering a course jointly sponsored by the departments of women studies and physics in the college of arts and sciences and by the college of engineering and was submitted to appropriate committees.[1]

Once approved, a seminar was organized for advanced undergraduate and graduate students in sciences, social sciences, and engineering. The course addressed issues relevant to full participation by ethnic minorities and women in science and engineering. Equal importance was given to the examination of barriers to participation, the effectiveness of solutions being tried in various campuses across the United States, and challenging students to think of old and new solutions in policy terms.

The intellectual framework focusing on equity and access issues was partly dictated by the institutional climate. We made a conscious effort to focus on change and improvement both past and future, as reflected in the three organizing themes for the course: overview of status of ethnic minorities and women in science and engineering, climate issues and successful interventions, and policy review and agenda for action. An effective examination of these topics requires multiple perspectives. The seminar was therefore co-led by a social scientist and a physical scientist. We expanded on these perspectives by inviting both national and local scientists and policy makers as speakers.

Both of us had chaired the committees for women in each of our respective professional associations (American Psychological Association and American Physical Society). Since 1994, Ginorio had offered through the department of women studies a 400-level course, "Women and/in Science," addressing feminist critiques of science. Ginorio's work with American Indian, Latina, and white girls from rural areas in Washington motivated her to offer a more policy-focused and action-oriented course. The department of physics was and is committed to increasing the number of women in the department at both the student and the faculty level. Thus, disciplinary and institutional strands entered into the intellectual goals that shaped this course.

LEARNING GOALS

We set four learning goals for all class activities:

- inform students of issues faced by ethnic minorities and women in science and engineering nationally and locally;

- introduce students to expert women and ethnic minority practitioners of science as well as expert social scientists who study issues faced by ethnic minorities and women in science and engineering;

- provide a national as well as local context for these issues so that students can critically evaluate the framing of the issues as well as the effectiveness of the solutions proposed so far; and

- prepare students to address these issues in the context of their own discipline and institution by developing a review of possible solutions at the University of Washington.

In the introduction of the course we clarified that women and men of color as well as white women would be the focus of the course and explained why. We also drew distinctions among the terms used such as "women" (vs. gender, feminine, feminist), "ethnic minorities" (vs. race, "protected," underrepresented), and science (the methods, the fields). The problematics of categories (such as the elision of women of color from the term "women and ethnic minorities" and how saying "ethnic minorities and women" may alleviate but not resolve that elision) and statistics (such as the omission from many statistics of Asian Americans) were also noted.[2] We made clear to the students that the critique of science would engage in and focus on access and discrimination issues rather than epistemological questions. We also prepared the students for interactions with national and local speakers to maximize their interactions with these experts and role models. After the lecture, which was open to the public, the speakers met with the seminar students for one hour.

The national speakers provided not only their expertise across disciplines but also provided a wide range of models of careers; from engineers who are associate deans of engineering to sociologists who do research on the practice of science. Furthermore, their expertise had been gained through a diversity of life trajectories. For example, Shirley Malcom was the first African American to receive a degree in zoology from the University of Washington; she then went on to gain a Ph.D. in environmental science and currently serves as director of education and resources at the American Association for the Advancement of Science (AAAS).

Overviews provided the students with a picture of the current status of ethnic minorities and women across the disciplines as well as some historical and policy context for that information. Woven through each topic were facts and statistics paired with critical feminist analyses. The course also sought to make more visible to the student the aspects of the life of the person behind the research. The bulk of the students' presentations were on climate issues. Local speakers presented interventions initiated and/or implemented at the University of Washington to address those same issues. Psychosocial topics, such as role models and mentors and expectations for achievement due to differential socialization, were included with more sociocultural concepts such as teaching and learning styles, climate, stereotypes, and nepotism rules.

The third section of the seminar focused on influencing public policy nationally, at the state level, and at the University of Washington and the actions that could be designed to address the issues examined in the seminar. The students were challenged to identify a pressing issue and then develop a policy recommendation to present a decision maker at any of these levels.

READINGS

The texts for the class emerged from three sources as the course progressed: professors, the speakers, and the students themselves. We assigned some readings that were eventually supplemented by readings suggested by each invited speaker. Students then were required to select assigned readings for their presentations after

73

consultation with the instructors. Most of the readings were then provided through the webpage set up for the class (URL), or placed in reserve in the main library and the department of physics library.[3] For a full set of the readings assigned, see faculty.washington.edu/olmstd/mwse/.

ASSIGNMENTS.

Assignments were chosen keeping in mind the composition of the class and the typical experiences with methods of students taking women studies or physics classes. The class was about equally divided among science and engineering students, and social science and liberal arts students. About half of the students were older than twenty-two years, and one-fifth were students of color; there was only one male in the class. Students registered for the course as either a physics (Physics 428, 3 credits) or women studies (Women 485, 5 credit) elective; almost two-thirds registered to receive physics credit. Which option they chose depended on whether they needed social science distribution courses (which Women 485 would fulfill) or science electives (which physics would fulfill). It also depended on whether they had the time to do the additional work (a final project) that the five-credit women studies course demanded.

We assumed that students came to this class with some introductory knowledge about feminism and science.[4] This was a reading, writing, and discussion course which had four major requirements for physics credit students and five major requirements for women studies credit students:

1. participating in class discussion, (15% of final grade);

2. leading/facilitating a class presentation, (30% of final grade, partly by peer evaluation);

3. preparing three short reports (45% of final grade);

4. summary of *one* of the panels or visiting speakers (10% of final grade);

5. (for 5-credit students only): doing a final project and corresponding paper.

In addition, all students were required to use e-mail and the course web site not only to obtain materials but also to post information they had gathered as well as to evaluate the class presentations.

Three of the assignments were typical for social science college courses: class participation, making a class presentation, and summarizing the presentation by a guest speaker or panel of speakers. A fourth assignment was specifically designed to fit this class: preparing three mini-reports. In the format, if not the content, these reports were akin to the homework regularly assigned to physics students. In this assignment we deliberately chose two modes of gathering information and producing knowledge that had been associated with the "sciences" and "women's studies" respectively: report on a "number" and its significance, and write a critical personal reflection on climate issues. We wanted all students to do a graded activity rooted in their own discipline, and to do so with awareness that both quantitative and qualitative modes of gathering information can yield useful data. In addition, we required a third report written as a "policy memo" addressed to a decision maker and which we urged the students to submit to that person or body.

For the "number" report, the students were to collect two kinds of numbers related to the course: one that could be measured at least five times (for example, number of ethnic minorities in biology at the University of Washington during each of the last five years), and another which was based on one instance (for example, the date on which a person had made a significant contribution). The students liked the immediacy of the results they obtained individually. When the results were presented collectively, such interesting results were obtained that it justified two additional activities towards the end of the class. We asked students to choose a science or engineering department for which they would collect current information about the number of ethnic minorities and women at both faculty and student levels. We also asked them to collect as much historical information about the participation of ethnic minorities and women in that department as was possible. This collection of numbers provided evidence at the departmental level of the impact of historical developments (such as Civil Rights legislation or the elimination of anti-nepotism regulations) and identified individuals who had "made history." Many current ethnic minority and women faculty members were among those identified as "making history."

To share this information with the whole campus, a reception was held in conjunction with the visit by the last national speaker to celebrate "the trailblazing women and ethnic minorities" the students had identified through their research (Ginorio and Olmstead 1999). The deans of arts and sciences and engineering officially hosted the reception that was supported by a grant from the office of the provost. All the faculty members in science and engineering departments were invited to this reception as were all the chairs of science and engineering departments, as well as all the provost-level and above decision makers at the university. Students had a chance to mingle with people who were literally making history in science at our university and with those who were making policy. Information about the "first" and "only" was posted in the walls of the hall.

The second mini-report, the personal reflection, provided an opportunity for most students to share with us the range of experiences they had had with science instructors and peers since primary school. Students seemed to relish the chance to vent about negative experiences and, for those who were science or engineering majors, to express their commitments to their chosen majors in spite of these experiences. This report provided us with specific points from which to address climate issues.

Students wrote memos on a broad range of topics. Social science students tended to address their memos to individuals at the state level or to address the problem at the macro-level, while physical science students tended to address their memos to local decision makers or to address the problems at the micro-level. We did not request that students inform us if they actually sent their memos. We did learn, however, that three of the memos were submitted, all from female majors in physics, all addressed to decision makers within the university, and all addressing issues at the micro-level.

Two undergraduate physics majors combined their memos into one addressed to the chair of the physics department. These students urged the chair to enact changes in the welcoming orientation program to make it friendlier to women students. The chair responded that he would work with these students and the Society of Physics Students to address their suggestions. The second memo that produced an immediate response was addressed to the dean of the graduate school and documented the need for a parental leave policy for graduate students. In response to that memo the dean of the graduate school appointed a Committee Task Force which examined the issues and almost a year later submitted a recommendation that graduate students be awarded parental leave (A copy of the report can be found at depts.washington.edu/gsatf/). An article based on this memo was published in the American Physical Society's Committee on the Status of Women in *Physics Gazette* (McCormick 2000).

TEACHING TECHNIQUES.

Both of us were in the classroom every time the course met, even when we were not leading that day's discussion. It was important that we provide the students with the vision of collaboration between a social scientist and physical scientist on an ongoing basis. That meant that we did not reap the "benefit" that some team-teaching professors have of being physically absent from the classroom on days when they are not the teacher in charge. The benefit that we did reap was that of learning from each other and the guest speakers and of following closely the students' responses so that we could prevent anticipated problems, such as student demoralization. As a result, students seemed comfortable approaching either one of us, and some consistently visited both of us during our respective office hours.

We challenged students to use their own experiences as a source of information but at the same time not to generalize from their own individual experiences. We were particularly mindful of this regarding the experiences that females may have had in science classrooms since research indicates that there are still many negative experiences with science. It was harder for those students who have had negative experiences not to generalize.

For some activities students worked in pairs or groups. We did not control the formation of such groups. Students tended to team up with people in their own discipline, particularly for the class presentation. The differences in quality of presentations, however, was not determined by discipline but by maturity.

Challenge of Interdisciplinary Work, Team Teaching

THE AUTHORS MET TEN years ago at an annual "beginning of the year" reception for women faculty members co-hosted by the Office of Affirmative Action and the Women's Center. Those yearly encounters led only to a warm but casual acquaintance until Ginorio developed the proposal. Seeking a colleague and a department that would be open to the idea, Professor Olmstead came to mind. In an earlier exchange, Olmstead had noted that there were fewer than 100 tenured women faculty members in Ph.D.-granting departments of Physics in the U.S.[5] Thus, our knowledge of each other was so superficial that we began this collaboration anticipating disagreements because of our distinct disciplinary bases. As we talked to each other, we also anticipated disagreements because of our very different cultural and class backgrounds. We assumed that deep philosophical differences would become evident once we were enmeshed in the daily exchange in our offices and the classroom.

On the first day of classes we told students to expect disagreements and prepared the ground for being able to do so in public without undermining the importance of what we were doing. To our surprise the disagreements never materialized in public or in private. The ongoing communication we had may have allowed us enough space to explore our differences before they were unbridgeable. Because we had to invite national speakers, we began meeting at least six months before the class began, and while we were teaching, we met a minimum of two times per week in addition to our classroom time. Perhaps our use of numbers as a basis for measurement (constructed as they may be) enabled us to understand each other's points. It could also be that the experience of having chaired the committee on women in each of our respective professional associations (American Psychological Association's Committee on Women and American Physical Society's Committee on the Status of

Women in Physics) gave us a common set of questions framed in the language of policy. It is possible, too, that commonality flowed from a more personal level. Having similar nuclear family configurations placed parallel demands on us as we daily juggled children, partners, families, teaching, research, and service. These experiences may have facilitated not only our understanding of some of the issues we were teaching about but also of each other.

It was important that we took each other seriously as scholars and as people for whom personal lives were important. We cared for our students and shared similar views on how to actively involve them in the course. It was also fun devising the activities that students would do for class. We learned from each other not only the content we were teaching but also the finer points of the process of enacting change within our own departments and in the institution as a whole. After the course, we kept in touch, have collaborated in some institutional policy issues, and are looking forward to the next time when we will teach the class.

On the negative side, Olmstead had to teach this course as an overload. Students so appreciated her efforts that they successfully nominated Olmstead for the University of Washington's Society of Physics Students' Undergraduate Teaching Award.

Course Impact on Students, University and Beyond

STUDENTS

TYPICALLY, WHEN STUDENTS TAKE courses that deal with discrimination and prejudice, they often feel demoralized by the magnitude of the challenges being discussed. That was not the case for our students. Contrary to their own expectations that they would feel depressed or discouraged by learning about barriers to the participation of ethnic minorities and women in science, students, who were science and engineering majors, reported feeling encouraged, and even more positive about their commitment to science. One social science major (a woman of color) decided to dismiss previous fears about declaring a concentration in science and became an environmental science major. Instead of feeling deflated, another student, a graduating senior, simply felt more energized to seek improvements. She wrote an article based on her policy memo that was published in a professional newsletter (McCormick 2000).

We attribute this sense of empowerment on the part of most of the students to three things. First, the negative information presented about existing barriers was countered by information about social and historical context and successful interventions. Most vividly, the chance to meet the "scientists and engineers who have

78

made history at the University of Washington" who were present at the reception honoring them had given the students many role models to choose from (Ginorio and Olmstead 1999). Second, writing policy memos gave the students an opportunity to *do* something concrete about the barriers that they had studied. The policy memo also gave them a tool to analyze the barriers and propose solutions. Finally, the presence in the classroom of two women scientists (representing the disparate fields of social and physical sciences) provided a closer view of the lives of professional scientists, involved and active in their disciplines not only at the level of scholarship but also of policy. We consciously provided students with an interdisciplinary experience that made our personal lives more visible to them than is typical in physics classes. They could see that we were struggling with our multiple roles, prioritizing them daily, and finding satisfaction not only in doing science but also in dismantling barriers to it. Because students graduated with a different vision of the possibilities for themselves and for others, we are confident that the impact of the course will last long after they leave the University of Washington.

UNIVERSITY

The course also led to tangible results at the institutional level. The first outcome is that both the women's studies and the physics departments have approved this course as a permanent one. The second measurable outcome is that through the panels of local experts and the Trailblazers' reception, people are far more aware of the rich information and expertise available through local resources.[6] Some presenters met each other through this course, while the reception provided a welcome opportunity for many other people with similar interests in these issues to meet for the first time.

Less concrete but an equally vital immediate impact of this course on the institution was the visibility it gave to what ethnic minorities and women in science and engineering routinely face. The context for contemporary barriers has been greatly influenced by two external events. The first was the passage by the voters of the state of Washington of Initiative 200. It states: "The state shall not discriminate against, or grant preferential treatment to, any individual or group on the basis of race, sex, color, ethnicity, or national origin in the operation of public employment, public education, or public contracting." Decisions about how to implement this initiative, popularly known as "the Anti-Affirmative Action Initiative," were being made at the time the course was being offered. The second event was the "MIT Report on Women Faculty" (MIT Faculty Newsletter 1999) released just days before the beginning of the course. The national experts who came to the university to speak on issues being

79

faced by ethnic minorities and women at this time gained an appreciation for the university's struggles in this area. The presence of chairs, directors of national programs, and other top-ranked administrators in the audience of the public lectures simultaneously signaled the serious commitment of the university and made evident that these administrators were being informed about cutting-edge approaches.

It is also clear through hindsight that the impact of the course on the university as a whole was significantly greater because our lecture series included national speakers. Without that resource, we believe we could not have had as great an influence. The presence of national speakers gave us the opportunity to invite the highest university administrators to introduce the speakers. Introductions were made by a regent, the president, a vice-president, and three deans. All of them are in positions to make decisions about the issues under discussion. Half of these administrators stayed to hear the presentations, and even those that left asked to be kept informed about what they could do. We followed up on these requests for information with an end-of-the-course report. Following the format for the policy memo, we documented the local issues at the University of Washington, provided data relevant to each, and offered a series of recommendations. The course report was presented in person to the president, the divisional dean of social sciences (representing the dean of arts and sciences), the dean of undergraduate education, the divisional dean of science, and all science chairs in the college of arts and sciences. Since presenting our report, 20 percent of the recommendations have been implemented and work is ongoing on some of the others.

It is certainly harder to gain visibility without the advantage of having resources to invite national speakers. However, if one of the goals is to make institutional change, then it is critical to decide how best to do that, even without the leverage of national experts. We found that preparing an end-of-the-course report that includes recommendations is a pragmatic strategy for answering the often asked, "But what can we do about this issue?" The most recent demonstration of the impact of our efforts occurred when Dr. Shirley Jackson, president of Rensselaer Polytechnic Institute, was selected for a prestigious visiting professorship at our university.[7] During her stay in Seattle, Dr. Jackson, an expert in both physics and policy matters, will explore the challenges university presidents face when they are committed to eliminating barriers to the participation of ethnic minorities and women in science and engineering.

US

Teaching this course has had an impact on us in both our local and national roles. The expertise we each gained through the course as well as through our service as chairs of the committees on women of our professional associations made us more visible at many levels of our institution. We both have consulted with University of Washington administrators on a current initiative to improve the status of women science faculty at the university. Shortly after the course was taught, the Commission on the Advancement of Women and Minorities in Science, Engineering, and Technology Development, established by legislation introduced by Congresswoman Morella (R-MD), came to our city, and we participated in their deliberations.

Both of us have given talks informed by lessons we learned teaching this course (Ginorio 1999; Olmstead 2000). The course gave us courage to take risks as professors. We experimented with new assignments, incorporated policy dimensions into our course, and dared to cross disciplinary boundaries through team teaching. Like our students, we both feel emboldened to do even more.

Endnotes

1   While the College of Engineering supported the proposal there was not enough lead time to go through the institutional approval system so that Engineering students could gain Engineering credit for the class. Thus, the Engineering students registered in the class earned credit from either Physics or Women Studies. We feel that it is important for a course such as this to provide credit through the corresponding department.

2   Contrary to many official reports, Asian Americans were included in all topics of the course. Similarly, women of color were a focus of discussion even when many reports offer information on women or on ethnic minorities but not cross-tabulated so that statements could be made about women of color specifically.

3   The next time we offer this course (Winter Quarter of 2002) it is unlikely that we will have the resources to bring national speakers. However, we will select readings from what they suggested, as well as add materials from recent publications such as Campbell et al., *Access denied: Race, ethnicity and the scientific enterprise,* and the special issue of *Women's Studies Quarterly* on "Building Inclusive Science: Connecting Women's Studies and Women in Science and Engineering" edited by Rosser (2000).

4   A quantitative science course at the college level was a pre-requisite for the course.

5   Professor Olmstead was the ninetieth woman to receive tenure in a Ph.D. granting physics department in the U.S. The year she was tenured was a banner year with the number topping 100.

6   The public lectures were attended by approximately 200 people, the newspaper distributed to the 12,000 faculty and staff on campus carried several articles about this course. The student newspaper also published two articles on the course.

7   Dr. Shirley Jackson was the first African American female to receive a doctorate in theoretical solid state physics from MIT.

Works Cited

Campbell, Jr. G., R. Denes, and C. Morrison, eds. 2000. *Access denied: Race, ethnicity and the scientific enterprise*. NY: Oxford Press.

Rosser, S. 2000. Building inclusive science: Connection women's studies and women in science and engineering. *Women's Studies Quarterly,* 28:1-2, 271-295.

Ginorio, A. B. 1999. *The last ones will be the first ones: Women of color in science and engineering*. Closing keynote at the University of California Los Angeles Women of Color in Science conference. Los Angeles, CA.

Ginori, A. B., and M. Olmstead 1999. Invitation to "A celebration of distinction." Seattle, WA.

McCormick, E. 2000. Addressing inadequate measures for work and family balance in graduate school. *Physics Gazette,* 19:1, 5.

The MIT Faculty Newsletter. March 1999. MIT report on women faculty in science. 11, 4: available at web.mit.edu/fnl/women/women.html.

Olmstead, M. March 2000. Women in science: Impressions of a U.S. physicist. A paper presented at Forschungszentrum Juelich, Juelich, Germany.

Widnall. S. 1988. Voices from the pipeline. *Science,* 241: 1740-1745.

The Curriculum in Context: Campus Networks and Change

*Donna M. Hughes, Karen Stein, Lisa Harlow,
Lynne Derbyshire, Helen Mederer, Donna
Bickford, Joan Peckham, Mercedes Rivero-Hudec,
Bette Erickson, and Faye Boudreaux-Bartels*

Women's Studies and Curricular Change

The goal of women's studies' twenty-year-old curricular movement has been to broaden the scope of the curriculum and place the content in social and historical context. Women's studies was founded to be the academic arm of the women's movement, and from its inception, it has been a catalyst of curricular change. Women's studies courses and scholarship were to act as a complement and corrective to the lack of scholarship and misinformation about women in the mainstream curriculum (Hunter College Women's Studies Collective 1983). The purpose of a feminist education is to assist students in developing a consciousness of the world around them, to think critically, and to engage in progressive change.

As the scholarship on women grew, initiatives were undertaken to integrate this research on women into the curricula, starting with the humanities and social studies and moving into science and engineering (Hughes 1991). Bonnie Spanier et al. (1984), biologist, feminist scholar, and one of the pioneers of curricular change wrote:

> The integration of women's studies scholarship within and across disciplines has initiated a far-reaching and perhaps revolutionary transformation of traditional knowledge. Not only are women becoming part of the subject matter of disciplines where they were previously ignored, but research questions, methods of analysis, and traditional theoretical frameworks are being challenged. The very canons of literature, art, the natural sciences, and the social sciences are called into question as women's studies scholars expand the boundaries of their fields of inquiry and as integration efforts bring this new scholarship into traditional courses.

83

To this day, the process of curricular change continues to expand the horizons of feminist teaching and scholarship. After years of women's studies invoking curricular change in other disciplines, the critical focus turned to how the women's studies curriculum itself might change to address scientific literacy for women. Anne Fausto-Sterling (1992), biologist and author of feminist critiques of science, called for increased education on science in women's studies. She pointed out that many women's studies scholars and students lack knowledge about science and technology, yet numerous important scientific projects and fields need a feminist critical analysis. Feminist scholars and students who have the analytical theories and methods lack the scientific knowledge to understand the science and technology involved. She writes, "The essential challenge facing women's studies scholars: to face and overcome our reluctance to engage with the segment of human knowledge we call science."

According to the Association of American Colleges and Universities national project, *Women and Scientific Literacy Project: Building Two-Way Streets,* funded by the National Science Foundation, women are scientifically literate when they are able to "ask intelligent questions about scientific claims, to explore a scientific question with some fullness on one's own and collectively, and to make informed judgments along the way" (AAC&U 1999). This challenge has led to renewed work on the curriculum in women's studies.

Much has been written about the multitude of ways the content and pedagogy of science and engineering courses might change (Rosser 1990, 1993, 1995, 1997), and more papers on the inclusion of science in women's studies courses are developing (Mueth 1999). Less has been written about the context of curriculum change and the particularity of campus networks and events that motivate, hinder, and shape the evolving curriculum.

The curriculum doesn't exist in isolation. A curriculum is the product of the lives and work of faculty, students, and administrators. Thus, the curriculum evolves in a context of networks of people, a climate for new ideas and practices, and even the physical buildings and infrastructure of the campus. All of these factors, most of which will be unique to any department, college, or institution, come into play during efforts to revise the curriculum.

> Change never occurs in a vacuum. The problems of curriculum transformation, enormous in themselves, take on added difficulty when considering the institutions in which the integration effort is undertaken. (Spanier, et al. 1984)

At the University of Rhode Island (URI) there have been many activities concerning women in science, engineering, and the curriculum. The authors of this paper have learned that curricular changes that enhance the enrollment, education, and graduation of women students require a critical mass of women faculty and a work environment in which they can thrive personally and professionally. In addition, women need their health and the security that their work environment is safe. These issues relate back to the curriculum of women's studies because to understand environmental-related health concerns, women have to be able to understand and use scientific information to assist them in personal health decisions and to analyze possible environmental contamination around them.

This paper will examine the curriculum at the University of Rhode Island (URI) in this context: What motivated many of the women in women's studies, science, and engineering to get involved, and how did they become connected through networks that have stimulated curricular changes and campus wide change in the climate and environment for all students, faculty and staff? This paper will describe: 1) networks of women on campus; 2) the health concerns arising from a cancer cluster among women in one building on campus; 3) the discrimination against women in engineering; 4) the curricular changes in women's studies; and 5) organizing for change among women on campus.

Many of the recent activities at URI result from the convergence of a critical mass of people interested in women and other underrepresented groups in the sciences and engineering. Just as many women have contributed to these activities, so many women are participating in the authorship of this paper, which has come to be a conversation among many voices.

Networks of Women on Campus

AT THE UNIVERSITY OF Rhode Island there have been two sustained networks of women. Each one has a twenty to thirty year history. One network is composed of those in women's studies; the other is known as the "Women in Science" group.

WOMEN'S STUDIES

At the University of Rhode Island there is a tradition of creating courses through networks of women. In fact, the women's studies program grew out of a team-taught course organized by a group of ten faculty members. One of the first courses in women's studies, "Women and Society," taught in 1972, was developed and taught by a team of women. One of the members of the team, Winifred Brownell, now dean of the college of arts and sciences, says:

I was one of a collaborative community of women faculty members who taught the first offering of "Women and Society."[1] We were a great group! We taught it on an overload basis. As you might imagine, we had resistance from some of our male colleagues (crude jokes, disparaging remarks, etc.), and no encouragement that I can remember from the administration. However, as long as we were willing to work together and offer the course as an overload, they did not stop us. The program in women's studies grew out of the community that came together to prepare and offer the course.

The women's studies program became an official degree program in 1980, and it continued to expand its course offerings and affiliated faculty.

WOMEN IN SCIENCE LUNCH GROUP

The Women in Science lunch group began in the early 1980s. Grace Frenzel, psychologist of the counseling center, organized a series of workshops, including one on being the only woman in an otherwise all male work group. This topic was of particular interest to women in science. After the workshop, some women in science wanted to continue to meet, so Grace Frenzel organized a weekly brown bag lunch with focused discussions and speakers. Faculty, researchers, graduate students, and staff from four colleges attended on a regular basis.[2] After fifteen years of lunch meetings, the group ceased to meet because of organizer fatigue. In response, Bette Erickson, from the instructional development program, volunteered to convene the group again. Reformed with renewed energy, it now meets on a monthly basis. Over the years through this voluntary group, women in science and engineering found mentoring, a place to vent their frustrations and anger about the often hostile climate they faced in their departments, and a professional network where they received empathy from others who understood. Significantly, two staff members organized the "Women in Science" group.[3] As they undertook specific projects over time, their solid involvement in the women's group contributed to the organizing capacity of the networks.

NETWORKS BEGIN TO WORK TOGETHER

As a result of curriculum growth, by the spring of 1989, the women's studies program offered many courses in the arts, humanities, and social sciences, but none in the natural sciences. At that time Karen Stein, from English and women's studies, served as acting director of the women's studies program. She took that opportunity to develop the women's studies course, "Women and the Natural Sciences." Working through networks to build connections that provide the basis for the course, Karen Stein recalls:

I met with the Women in Science lunch group and was pleased to find them very excited about creating such a course. We met several times and put together a course outline based on the expertise and interests of some of these faculty members.[4] However, they explained that they could not teach the course, as their department chairmen (and they were all men) would consider it sociology and not an appropriate subject for their science department. Therefore, we agreed that I would convene the course, and they would be guest lecturers in it. At that time, faculty in the college of arts and sciences were being encouraged to create courses that bridged the humanities and sciences. The "Women and the Natural Sciences" course was offered first in 1990. After three years, because the course was successful, it was accepted as a women's studies course.

The topics addressed in the "Women and the Natural Sciences" course were the classic questions being asked by feminists: 1) Who are the women scientists and what have their career paths been? 2) How does science study women? 3) How is science taught and what are the implications of this for women students? 4) Would science be different if more women were scientists? and 5) Does a feminist critique of science exist?

To find bibliographies and readings for the new course, Karen Stein turned to her women's studies network.[5] She believes the course has been highly successful. As reported on anonymous questionnaires students not only develop greater interest in women and in science as a result of taking this course, they become more confident of their own academic abilities.

In the summer of 1990, Winifred Brownell, then in communication studies, and Karen Stein undertook a research project on the images of women scientists in popular films.[6] They viewed popular films featuring women scientists and produced a videotape with representative cuts. Karen Stein says, "Interestingly, we found that the plots of these films quickly turn from the work of the scientists to romance and/or adventure, with the men rescuing the women scientists."

During the 1990s, women's studies faculty grew more aware of the need to integrate the study of science into women's studies. In 1996, the women's studies program made a commitment to linking women's studies and science by hiring Donna M. Hughes—who has a Ph.D. in genetics and was doing work on integrating content on gender, race, class, and sexuality into science curricula—as the first Eleanor M. and Oscar M. Carlson Endowed Chair in women's studies.[7] Shortly after her arrival, Donna Hughes began to collaborate with other women at URI to develop grant proposals related to scientific literacy and curriculum development.

In 1997, the next big link between the two networks was made. Donna Hughes proposed a collaborative curricular project between women in women's studies and in science and engineering. Also in the same year, the URI Women's Studies, Science and Engineering Curriculum Project was launched as part of the Association of American Colleges and University's project, *Women and Scientific Literacy: Building Two Way Streets,* funded by the National Science Foundation. The three-year curriculum and faculty development initiative was designed to strengthen undergraduate science education for women. The goal was to make science more attractive to women by expanding the content and improving teaching methods of the science curriculum in higher education. The project focused on both science and engineering and on the women's studies curricula. The primary goal of the project was to build connections by incorporating the new scholarship in women's studies into the undergraduate science, engineering, and mathematics courses. In addition, women's studies courses began to include more science content. Through our efforts we aimed to graduate more women with science and engineering degrees and more scientifically literate women with women's studies degrees (Hughes 1997).

Cancer Cluster and Hostile Climate: Grounds for Action

AS WOMEN AND NETWORKS CAME together, two topics increasingly became the focus of their attention, and eventually grounds for collective action.

BREAST CANCER

Since 1992, an inordinate number of faculty and staff women have been diagnosed with breast cancer at URI. In one building alone there have been at least eleven cases of cancer out of 175 employees who work in the building, mostly breast cancer, and a high number of other unusual and sometimes serious ailments.

Seven women from Chafee Social Science Center were diagnosed with breast cancer between 1992-1994. A number of the women have been affiliated with women's studies. The possibility of a cancer cluster raised issues of building or environmental contamination. Shortly afterwards, a group of faculty on campus began organizing to request an epidemiological study of a possible breast cancer cluster. A consultant was hired to conduct the study, but was let go because of protests from the faculty group who felt the person was not qualified to conduct the study. Some testing of air quality and asbestos was conducted, resulting in asbestos abatement, but no other carcinogenic agents were tested for. Attempts were made to identify another consultant, and a survey was initiated to collect data from the campus community on the incidence of cancer. These latter efforts were never completed. Several years later, an eighth woman was diagnosed with breast cancer and about a dozen other cancers were diagnosed.

In the summer of 1996, one of the curriculum project participants, Dana Shugar, associate professor of English and women's studies, was diagnosed with breast cancer. Although her office was not in the building with the cancer cluster, her diagnosis brought the issue of breast cancer to the immediate attention of the women's studies faculty. When she died in January 2000, she was working on her second book, *The Other Epidemic: Lesbians Confront the Challenge of Breast Cancer.*

HOSTILE CLIMATE

On campus, many women—students, faculty and staff—have experienced a broad spectrum of experiences that comprise a chilly or hostile climate. Women have been adversely affected in many ways, large and small, such as scheduling of meetings at the close of the day, when women with family care responsibilities are unable to attend; addressing men by title, while addressing women by first name; inadequate laboratory space or funds; known sexual harassment that is left festering for years; "friendly" recommendations regarding marriage, divorce, pregnancy, socializing, dressing nicely, dressing badly, speaking up, not speaking up, if they want to get tenure or promotion; sexually explicit screen-savers that are considered a first amendment right in computer labs; women being told they don't have the right "style" to be a department chair; and lack of annual reviews that leave women uncertain about their progress toward tenure because the contractual annual review process is not followed. Over the years, the college of engineering became known as a hostile place for women. There were many stories about the chilly climate, and a number of women faculty members and graduate students had left over time. In 1997, there were only three women out of sixty-eight faculty members in the college of engineering.

Although concerns about breast cancer, environmental contamination, and chilly professional climate for women scientists and engineers are common themes throughout the country, these issues coalesced in a particular way at URI, mainly through women's networks that have had widespread impact on the campus and on the curriculum.

Women's Studies Increasing Focus on Health and Science

FROM 1997 TO THE present, the Women's Studies, Science, and Engineering Curriculum Project has sponsored conferences, speakers, reading groups, and curriculum development projects.[8] All have focused on the combination or intersection of women/gender, science, engineering, or health, and all drew participants from across the campus. As a result of the increasing concerns both about cancer among women and about the hostile climate for women in science and engineering, speakers who illuminated these topics were often chosen.

One speaker seemed to resonate with the campus concerns. Sandra Steingraber, ecologist, poet, cancer survivor, and author of *Living Downstream: An Ecologist Looks at Cancer and the Environment* seemed to embody all the issues. Since her presentation, Steingraber's book has been used in two women's studies courses: "Feminist Methods," and "Women and the Natural Sciences." In the introduction to women's studies course, Donna Bickford has added readings on breast cancer and the environment and discusses with the students why lifestyle practices, family histories, and genetics are emphasized but environmental pollution ignored. She says, "Not only does this demand that students interrogate assumptions of 'scientific objectivity' and 'truth,' but it encourages them to strategize about activist interventions."

Other women's studies courses added topics on women/gender, science, and health. For example, Donna Hughes, added the topic of women's health and nuclear testing in the South Pacific to her "International Women's Issues" course[9] and feminist critiques of the scientific method and impact of development polices and reproductive technologies on women to her "Introduction to Feminist Theory" course.[10] Dana Shugar added a focus on multiculturalism and science to the senior course, "Critical Issues in Feminist Scholarship."[11] Donna Bickford added papers by Ann Fausto-Sterling and Fatimah Jackson, both of whom were speakers at the curriculum conferences.[12]

Other speakers and events sponsored by the women's studies program also addressed women, science, and health. In Fall 1997, Susan Love, physician and co-author of the *Doctor Susan Love's Breast Book* and *Doctor Susan Love's Hormone Book: Making Informed Decisions about Menopause,* spoke on "Women's Health: The Need to Tell the Truth." As part of this event, a panel of breast cancer survivors described their personal experiences in fighting cancer.[13] The panel members ranged in age from thirty to sixty and came from different parts of the campus: two of the women were among the highest-ranking administrators on campus, two were faculty members, and two were staff members. Two of the women were also participants in the curriculum project. They were at different stages in their cancers from still in treatment to thirteen years post-diagnosis. All of the women said they felt ill-equipped to make the decisions that came with a cancer diagnosis. They, along with their friends and family, ferreted out technical literature on breast cancer to assist them in making choices about surgery and treatment. After searching the literature on cancer treatment, one of the scientists said she had to withstand "the wrath" of her doctors when she opted for a newly developed, less-known treatment, instead of "the standard of care." The women described the courage and determination they needed to face the cancer diagnosis and treatment because, after all the options and implications were presented to them, they had to make the decisions themselves. As a result of their experience, each woman felt called upon to help others who were struggling with breast cancer.

After the panel, a female graduate student said to a panelist, "I came expecting to listen to all of you talk about how horrible cancer was for you, and instead, everybody seems to be very upbeat, talking about the important life lessons you learned from this experience." Margaret Leinen, then dean of the graduate school of oceanography and now head of the National Science Foundation Geosciences Directorate, said:

> That comment summarized the feeling that I had about cancer survivors before having cancer myself, as well as the feeling that I had toward the end of my treatment. It was wonderful for me that the panel could convey their individual and collective strength and that it could reassure members of the audience.

The altruism of the women united that day in a way which transcended discipline or rank. In reflecting on those events, Lisa Harlow wrote:

> Looking back over the events and discussions during that day in 1997, there is little doubt that a web of far-reaching connections was built, linking science, women's health, and the need for collaborative efforts across multiple disciplines, communities, and frameworks.

WOMEN'S STUDIES STUDENTS PROPOSE A COMMISSION ON THE STATUS OF WOMEN

The senior women's studies course, "Critical Issues in Feminist Scholarship," taught by Dana Shugar, has always included a class project. By then, there was growing awareness that changes were needed, but there was no university-wide women's group to address them. The students researched the topic and found that URI was the only state university in New England that did not have a commission for women. They collected the information on the different configurations, compositions, and mission statements from commissions throughout New England. At the end of the semester they made a presentation to the president and provost, proposing the establishment of a URI Commission on the Status of Women. The proposal was accepted, although by Spring 2001, the Commission has yet to be convened.

Lynne Derbyshire, from communication studies and women's studies, co-taught the course with Dana Shugar that semester. The Spring 1999 class turned out to be the last time Dana Shugar taught this course. Lynne Derbyshire writes:

In the spring of 1999, as Dana Shugar was combating breast cancer, I was asked to team teach "Critical Issues in Feminist Scholarship" with her. The students were required to design, implement, and evaluate a project based on activism rooted in feminist theory. The outcome of the assignment was a proposal for the creation of a Commission on the Status of Women. I found this connection between theory and activism very exciting and learned new lessons about how to achieve change in the university.

WOMEN'S STUDIES STUDENTS REPORT ON CANCER AND THE ENVIRONMENT

At the beginning of Spring semester 2000, Dana Shugar died of breast cancer at age thirty-nine, less than four years after her diagnosis. In memory of Dana Shugar, the students decided to make their group project a research report on breast cancer and the environment in Rhode Island.[14] At the end of Spring 2000, they published "Breast Cancer and the Environment: The Real Story." The 18-page booklet spans the range from scientific to the artistic. It includes the scientific, the personal, the political, the objective, and the subjective. It includes artwork, poems, facts on environmental contamination and cancer, a list of polluters in Washington County (where URI is located) and Superfund sites (Washington County has three), facts that dispel myths about breast cancer, personal lifestyle recommendations for prevention and early detection of breast cancer, instructions on how to do a self-examination, and a list of Rhode Island resources.

The report opens with a tribute to Dana Shugar, who "urges us to think and process; understand and ask questions. She inspired each of us to look inside ourselves and challenge what we found there. ... Dana Shugar made us want to conquer the universe. She made us want to fight for ourselves and also fight for others." Lauren Holt, women's studies minor, wrote this about her experience in working on the student project:

> I think last year's [2000] events opened up a whole new level of consciousness of cancer. ... Dana Shugar was to be my "Critical Issues in Feminist Scholarship" professor that year. I had three classes with her until she had to go. ... Reading *Living Downstream* by Sandra Steingraber, doing research in the Peace Dale Public Library on the EPA test results of our local area, the PCBs in the Chafee Building, learning about the professors with cancer, and Dana Shugar's death, all just seemed to fit together the big jigsaw puzzle in my head. For the first time, I was actually scared to breathe the air around me and to drink the water in my home. Even the organic foods that I spend the extra money on seemed to be null and void. The phrase "there's nowhere to run and there's nowhere to hide" seemed to echo in my head. ... Do we sit back and watch our world be further infected with disease by chemical corporations, toxic waste, insecticides, and ani-

mal wastes from factory farming on a daily basis? Do we wait for NASA to discover other habitable planets so that when we destroy this one, we can move on to another planet? ...I have hope when I see students working together to raise the level of consciousness in others. I have hope when I hear someone mention the name Rachel Carson. I have hope when authors continue to write about the subject. And I have hope when people...actually do something about it!

Students were empowered not only within the context of courses, but in the cocurricular arena as well. Many women students had either been students of Dana Shugar in the past or were interested in activism related to women's health. In Spring 2000, students from POWER (People Organized for Women's Equality and Resilience) organized a conference entitled *Breast Cancer Awareness Conference*.[15] The announcement stated that the conference was organized because of "Dana Shugar's strong influence on our education and experience as students at URI." The campus community was encouraged "to join the crusade to bring awareness to women about breast cancer." The keynote speaker was Marlene McCarthy of the Rhode Island Breast Cancer Coalition.

Networking to Improve the Campus Climate for Women

A NUMBER OF THE speakers sponsored by the curriculum project focused on the climate for women in science and engineering and advocated organizing to bring about the desired changes in science, engineering, and women's studies. Ramesh Seprehrrad, worldwide technical program manager for Xerox Engineering Systems, spoke about her own experiences as a woman of color in national and international corporate settings in her talk, "Leadership in Science and Technology." As a young woman, she quickly established a rapport with the students from engineering and science who met with her for lunch. Fatimah Jackson, professor of zoology and anthropology at the University of Maryland–College Park, gave a talk entitled "Changing the Scientific Paradigm: Lessons Learned from the Human Genome Project." After her compelling scientific and political analysis, someone asked her what can be done to change things. Dr. Jackson leaned over the podium and said, "You resist!"

Consciousness and frustration with problems on campus was reaching a critical point. From the perspective of the curriculum project, changes for women in science and engineering can't be made without women. To improve the climate for women or revise the courses and pedagogy, faculty members who are committed to recruiting and retaining women are needed.

CHANGING THE CLIMATE FOR WOMEN IN ENGINEERING

In the spring of 1996 there were three women out of sixty-eight faculty members in the college of engineering: one of them was hired that year as a tenure-track assistant professor, another was an untenured assistant professor, and the third was a full professor. At the end of the 1997–1998 academic year, the most recently hired female faculty member left the university. Because the level of hostility towards her was so great, she asked for a faculty witness from outside the college to attend her exit interview with the dean. In September 1998, the American Association of University Professors (AAUP) filed a grievance against the college's dean, Tom Kim, on behalf of the women faculty members in the college of engineering.

The two remaining faculty women were members of the Women in Science group and active participants in the curricular projects. According to Mercedes Rivero-Hudec, "It was a lengthy process and highly taxing on the complainants." During the eighteen months process, the chilly climate within the college of engineering increased. "Silence was the modus operandi. With very few exceptions, no other engineering faculty members questioned what was going on and why," said one of the complainants, because the dean had called for a "pseudo" gag order. Outside the college of engineering, there was more concern and awareness of the seriousness of the situation, and more people were willing to talk to the women involved in the grievance.

One of the topics introduced at the Women in Science lunch group was "Supportive Environments: What Do Women Need in Order to Thrive as Scientists?" This discussion continued over time and increasingly focused on the climate in the college of engineering. Lisa Harlow, from psychology, explains: "We kept hearing over and over stories of women's harassment, of a hostile climate for women. We just couldn't stand it anymore. We had to do something." Soon, the Women's Equity Committee was formed. The committee drafted a petition to the University of Rhode Island president and provost that described the chilly campus climate and presented a list of changes that needed to be addressed. Over 130 people at URI signed the petition.

The Women's Equity Committee began meeting with President Robert Carothers and Provost M. Beverly Swan on a broad range of issues. The committee urged consciousness raising about the hostile climate at URI, particularly in some programs; helping to ensure a resolution to the mediation process in engineering; attending to pornographic screens in engineering labs; establishing a Commission on the Status of Women; creating a new women's center; reviving the sexual harassment committee; engaging the Affirmative Action office in gender equity and in major campus searches; testing for possible cancerous agents at URI and an epidemiological study of a possible cancer cluster; and establishing a subcommittee to investigate inequities in salary, workload, and facilities.

Because the engineering grievance was still unresolved and the months-long adversarial process was taking an emotional toll on the complainants, the Women's Equity Committee decided to focus on that issue alone in its February 2000 meeting with the president and provost. The committee pressed for the president to intervene to bring a fast, acceptable resolution to the engineering grievance. The women intended to send a message to the university administration that many women across campus were watching the proceedings and were concerned about the outcome. In response to the pressure from the faculty union (AAUP) and the Women's Equity Committee, as well as an upcoming arbitration deadline, within one month the grievance was resolved in the women's favor.

In March 2000, President Robert L. Carothers acknowledged that there is a climate hostile to women in the college of engineering and agreed to a number of corrective actions. In a statement, President Carothers said that,

> Thomas J. Kim, dean of the college of engineering, 'bears prime responsibility for the climate in the college. He has not challenged those whose actions contributed to this climate…He has not assured that women on the faculty are treated equitably and fairly. We believe that women faculty have been adversely affected professionally by the hostile climate toward women [in engineering]. Some believed it necessary to resign their positions and pursue their professional lives elsewhere.' (McVicar, 25 March 2000)

In part, in recognition of her leading role in mentoring women students and fighting sex discrimination in the college of engineering, in April 2000, the URI Association of Professional and Academic Women named Faye Boudreaux-Bartels their "Woman of the Year."[16] She received an enthusiastic standing ovation at the awards dinner.

As a result of the sexual harassment grievance settlement in the college of engineering, an independent audit team visited the University of Rhode Island during Fall 2000 to examine the climate in the college of engineering, identify tangible and intangible factors that retard the achievement of full professional equality, and recommend effective remedial measures.[17] The final report was released in December 2000.[18] It lists a number of factors that:

> …contributed to a belief that some male professors and administrators did not view female colleagues as equals but rather as second-class members of the fac-

ulty. Adding to the women's discomfort was their perception that individuals who raised complaints about disparate treatment were viewed as 'troublemakers,' a perception that discouraged them from seeking redress for mistreatment.

Among the negative factors cited by the independent audit team were:

- Demeaning and insulting statements and remarks made by the dean and faculty members toward women faculty;

- 'Window dressing' efforts by the dean to support women in engineering programs rather than providing adequate funding for such efforts;

- Public treatment of women faculty in a less respectful manner than male faculty, such as addressing the women by the first names and the men by their title and last names;

- Commenting to women faculty on the perceived appropriateness of their clothing;

- The failure to carry out annual performance reviews in the manner specified in the collective bargaining agreement.

The audit recommended changes in 1) recruitment and hiring, 2) retention of faculty, and 3) communications and education strategy. Most significantly, the audit team recommended that URI select a new dean supportive of gender equity and skilled in dealing with gender and diversity issues. In addition, the report recommended:

- The recruitment of a 'critical mass' of female faculty, including at the senior level, through the addition of new lines;

- Develop steps to insure the retention of female faculty, including providing adequate start-up funds, competitive salaries, helpful mentoring, fair evaluation and supportive departmental leadership;

- Improve communications about gender equity issues so that faculty can deal openly and fairly with issues raised by the presence of female faculty members.

Networking for Women's Health

ALTHOUGH THE WOMEN'S EQUITY Committee addressed a broad range of issues at URI, one long-standing worry was about cancer and the fear of environmental contamination. Many people, especially those with offices and classrooms in the Chafee

Building, were unsatisfied with previous testing and university response. The organizing process has been a collective effort from many facets of campus, ranging from faculty, staff, and students to the administration and off-campus consultants. In 1999/2000, the Women's Equity Committee asked President Carothers to undertake testing at present day standards that would satisfy the campus. A petition sent to the president described the frustration of the people in Chafee Building:[19]

> When health concerns began to be expressed at least ten years ago, university officials arrived at a premature conclusion that these concerns did not warrant any examination of the building. Six years ago, when that conclusion could not be sustained due to the continuation of cancer diagnoses, the university reached another premature conclusion when it decided that a narrow screening process was warranted. If the university had conducted a thorough screening process six years ago, six years of continuing cancer diagnoses, uneasiness, and lack of trust might have been avoided. This lack of validation, lack of response, and lack of respect for the rational concerns about the health and safety of the building has led also to the lack of trust that characterizes the feeling of many faculty and staff.

Later, President Robert Carothers thanked Helen Mederer, one of the authors of the petition, for "articulating clearly the concerns of affected staff."

As a result of activism by the Women's Equity Committee, during fall semester 2000, more thorough environmental testing was conducted in the Chafee Social Science Center, the largest classroom and office building on campus. The test results showed unacceptable levels of polychlorinated biphenyls (PCBs) in some area of the building—more than eight times the legally acceptable limits. PCBs are a group of manufactured organic chemicals that were used widely as coolants and lubricants in transformers, capacitors, and other electrical equipment (Agency for Toxic Substances and Disease Registry 1997). In 1977, their manufacturing stopped in the United States because of evidence that they build up in the environment and cause a variety of health effects, including cancer and immune suppression. According to the Environmental Protection Agency, PCBs are the sixth most carcinogenic environmental pollutant. Little is known about the long-term health effects of PCBs on humans.

Five days after the release of these findings, the Chafee Social Science Center was closed, displacing a significant portion of the faculty and staff on campus. An internal scientific advisory committee made up of scientists from around the university was appointed. This advisory committee oversees the environmental consulting company and is ensuring that in their testing, they use state-of-the-art scientific methods and standards. In addition, the Centers for Disease Control and Prevention and the Environmental Protection Agency have become involved in resolving the contamination issues.

The Women's Equity Committee took a leading role in pressing for further testing of the building. At times, some have asked if building contamination is a gender issue. Ostensibly, women have been disproportionately affected insofar as the majority of cancers have been breast cancer. Additionally, women are primarily affected because many women who work in the building are mothers and gestated and breast fed their children while employed in the building. One of these women, Helen Mederer, from sociology and women's studies, gestated and breast fed her daughter while working in what is now known as literally the most toxic office. She remarks:

> I not only have to worry about my own health, but the health of my child as well. And I thought I had effectively answered the question about how my employment has affected my children! Finding out about the PCB contamination causes me great anguish, and I don't think people understand this point of view.

Breast milk is the major human-to-human transmission route of PCBs, and one of the first recommendations made to building residents by the environmental consulting company in charge of the building contamination studies was for breast feeding women to stop breast feeding their children. For mothers in this situation, there has been a perceived lack of sympathy from others. Thus, the issue of child health and occupational health and safety standards has emerged as another women in science initiative.

The Power of Networks to Create Change

THROUGH NETWORKING, THE WOMEN in science, engineering, and women's studies, have made significant changes in women's studies courses and in the lives of people on campus. Donna Hughes says,

> The most important thing I've done at URI is to connect already existing networks. ... Certainly, the recent outcomes achieved at URI are a case of the whole being far more than the sum of the parts. ... As a woman with a science background, now working in women's studies, I fit securely in both the "Women in Science" group and the women's studies group. Then I proposed projects in which they could work together. The energy released by that cooperation produced a wave of change for women at URI.

One measure of change is the evidence that women's studies courses have begun to include more science. In the process, they have drawn more science students to women's studies. The "Introduction to Women's Studies" course at URI has always drawn a wide range of students, because it fills a general education requirement in the social sciences. Since the beginning of the curriculum project, Donna Bickford has observed an increasing number of women with majors in science disciplines enrolling in the course. In previous years, most students came from the humanities or social sciences, but now there are science majors from marine biology, nursing, and pharmacy. This shift has made a difference both in the content of discussions and for individual students. Donna Bickford comments on her own response to the curriculum project:

> What has been particularly interesting to me about the curriculum project is that it did not just encourage more women to go into science, and did not only work to change the way science is taught, but insisted on the need to add a component of scientific literacy to women's studies courses. Since I am not a scientist, and have been scared of math since the second grade, this was my own personal challenge as an educator. If I had not had the opportunity to hear these speakers and understand the need for transformation to occur, I would not have had the knowledge or the confidence to include readings and discussion about scientific issues to my syllabus. I have learned from this project, and that means my students have the opportunity to learn.

To expand their curricular innovations even more, women in women's studies, science, and engineering have continued to enhance science education for undergraduate women at URI. In 2000, they designed four learning communities for students.[20] Each learning community is designed to assist women students through the times in their undergraduate careers that they are most likely to turn away from science, engineering, or technology. The learning community concept enables integration of material across disciplines to broaden and deepen students' learning experiences.

One of the learning communities, Writing and the Natural Sciences, clustered the women's studies course, "Women and the Natural Sciences" with "Introduction to Biology" (including a lab), Writing 101 (a composition course on writing about science), and URI 101, a course which introduces first semester students to the university and to being a successful student. As health and science issues unfold at URI, these topics are being incorporated into the curriculum. Karen Stein, organizer of this learning community and instructor for "Women and the Natural Sciences" comments:

> In light of the closing of Chafee Building as a result of high levels of PCBs, an important focus of the course this spring is the environment. We began the course with Rachel Carson's *Silent Spring,* and are studying how much pesticide use has grown since Carson's time.

99

Conclusion

THE EVENTS AND CHANGES at URI came about because women were connected with each other. The discussions and activities validated the feelings of many women and assured them that they were not unique, that the problems were systemic, and that group action could make a difference. The networks gave women a collective voice and a course of action that resulted in change.

Just as women's studies nationally grew out of coalitions of women seeking to combine activism with innovation in scholarship and pedagogy, so, too, the current coalition of women at URI is combining similar ingredients in their attempts to address curricular change, the status of women, and the campus environment (both psychological and physical). Their experiences as change agents demonstrate the importance of drawing on the tools of both the sciences and the social sciences to analyze and respond to a chilly—and unhealthy—campus climate. Their actions are strengthening the position of women on campus and providing role models of activism and coalition building for students and faculty alike.

Endnotes

1   Other team members included Bernice Lott, Psychology; Sharon Strom, History; Judith Anderson, Communication Studies; Karen Stein, English; Mathilda Hills, English; and Natalie Kampen, Art.

2   Women came from the colleges of arts and sciences, engineering, and pharmacy, and the graduate school of oceanography.

3   Grace Frenzel, psychologist, counseling center and Bette Erickson, instructional development program

4   Kat Quina, psychology and women's studies, lectured on math anxiety; Faye Boudreaux-Bartels, electrical engineering, spoke about women in engineering careers; Grace Frenzel, psychologist, counseling center, presented a slide show on minority individuals in the workplace; Joan Peckham, computer science, presented on women in computer science and statistics; Marilyn Harlin, biological sciences, spoke about Rachel Carson; and Gaby Kass-Simon, biological sciences, presented issues connected with abortion. In several years we had panels of women scientists describing their careers, including Phyllis Brown, chemistry; Margaret Leinen, oceanography; Mercedes Rivero-Hudec, chemical engineering; and Nancy Eaton, mathematics. Male faculty members participated as well: Jim Loy, sociology and anthropology, spoke about women primatologists; Breck Peters, sociology, about sociobiology, and Louis Kirschenbaum, chemistry, about women in chemistry.

5   Karen Stein says, "I did some research and found Sandra Harding's intriguing title *The Science Question in Feminism*. To develop a list of course readings, I conducted a library search using a bibliography of URI library resources in women's studies that Bernice Lott, psychology and women's studies, had compiled."

6   The project was funded by a small grant from the University of Rhode Island Foundation.

7   This appointment was made possible through a $1 million endowment from Eleanor M. Carlson, a URI staff member who wrote that she had a "great passion for matters which affect the status of women in our society" (http//:www.uri.edu/artsci/wms/hughes/carlson.htm). She became involved in women's studies by taking a course on "Women and Aging." Later, she joined the women's studies council, a community-based group formed to support women's studies.

8   Funding to carry out these events and projects has come from the Association of American Colleges and Universities, the National Science Foundation, the Rhode Island Board of Governors for Higher Education, the URI Foundation, the URI Honors Program and Visiting Scholars Committee, the Rhode Island Partnership for Research on Women and Gender, and the offices of the provost, the dean of the college of arts and science, the dean of the college of engineering, the dean of the college of nursing, and the departments of English, biological sciences, and natural resources science.

9   Text used: *Daughters of the Pacific* edited by Zohl de Ishtar, Spinifex Press, 1994.

10 Text used: *Ecofeminism* by Maria Mies and Vandana Shiva, Zed Books, 1993.

11 Text used: *Is Science Multicultural?* by Sandra Harding, Indiana University Press, 1998.

12 Papers used: Fausto-Sterling, Anne. 2000. The Five Sexes: Why Male and Female Are Not Enough in *The Meaning of Difference*. Eds. Karen E. Rosenblum and Toni-Michelle C. Travis. Boston: McGraw Hill, 87-92; and Jackson, Fatimah. 1998. Scientific Limitations and Ethnical Ramifications of a Non-representative Human Genome Project: African American Responses. *Science and Engineering Ethics*. 4, 155-170.

13 Panel members were: Lisa Harlow, psychology; Dana Shugar, women's studies and English; Bobbi Koppel, director of career services; M. Beverly Swan, provost; Margaret Lienen, dean, graduate school of oceanography; and Rosita P. Chang, business center.

14 Lauren Holt, Sara Conway, Lynn Morelli, Brie Pendleton and Casey Brennan are the students who dedicated their group project to Dana Shugar.

15 Two students who played leadership roles in organizing the conference were Trisha Barkley, philosophy and women's studies, 2000 and Mary Peck, French and women's studies, 2000.

16 Faye Boudreaux-Bartels has many professional achievements. In 1999, in recognition of her research in electrical engineering, she was accepted as a Fellow of the Institute of Electrical and Electronics Engineers. At URI she helped mentor women engineering students through the Bridge program for incoming engineering majors and through the Society for Women Engineers.

17 The university's administration and the AAUP mutually agreed to hire Workplace Solutions, Ithaca, New York, to conduct the audit. Three members of Workplace Solutions visited the college of engineering on October 30 and 31, 2000, participating in approximately twenty meetings. They also followed up their visit to URI with telephone interviews and e-mails with university and college officials, as well as with faculty members. The cost of the independent audit was borne equally by the University of Rhode Island and the AAUP.

18 *Report of the Audit Team to the University of Rhode Island College of Engineering*

19 This petition was circulated after the results of the testing were released in response to the university priorities in the handling of the problem. In this paper it is placed out of chronological order.

20 "Multidisciplinary Science and Engineering Learning Communities for Students and Faculty" is funded by the National Science Foundation and the University of Rhode Island.

Works Cited

Annunziato, Frank R. 12 February 2000. College of engineering update, *URI AAUP News*, 27: 5.

Association of American Colleges and Universities. 1999. *Frequently asked questions about feminist science studies*. Washington, DC: Association of American Colleges and Universities.

Fausto-Sterling, Anne. 1992. Building two-way streets: The case of feminism and science, *NWSA Journal*, 4:3, 336-349.

Hughes, Donna M. Autumn 1991. Transforming science and technology: Has the elephant yet flicked its trunk? *NWSA Journal*, 3: 3.

Hughes, Donna M. 2 April 1997. Presentation to University of Rhode Island Dean's Council (unpublished).

Hunter College Women's Studies Collective. 1983. *Women's realities, women's choices: An introduction to women's studies*. New York: Oxford University Press.

McVicar, D. Morgan. 25 March 2000. URI admits bias against women professors. *Providence Journal*.

Mueth, Judith. 7 April 1999. Science in women's studies: Combining the scientific method, laboratory exercises and feminist epistemology. Presentation at University of Rhode Island conference, *Diversifying the Culture and Curriculum of Science, Engineering and Women's Studies.*

Rosser, Sue. 1990. *Female friendly science: Applying women's studies methods and theories to attract students to science.* New York: Teachers College Press.

Rosser, Sue. 1993. Female friendly science: Including women in curricular content and pedagogy in science. *Journal of General Education,* 42: 3, 191-220.

Rosser, Sue, ed. 1995. *Teaching the majority: Breaking the gender barrier in science, mathematics, and engineering.* New York: Teachers College Press.

Rosser, Sue. 1997. *Re-engineering female friendly science.* New York: Teachers College Press.

Spanier, Bonnie, Alexander Bloom, and Darlene Boroviak, eds. 1984. *Toward a balanced curriculum: A sourcebook for initiating gender integration projects.* Cambridge, Massachusetts: Schenkman Publishing Company.

Policy and Pedagogy

Section B
The Classroom as Laboratory:
Teaching Strategies and Student Reactions

What is Feminist Pedagogy? Useful Ideas for Teaching Chemistry

Catherine Hurt Middlecamp and
Banu Subramaniam

In our experience, scientists are likely to be newcomers to the scholarship that has arisen from the field of women's studies. This paper will examine one such area of scholarship, feminist pedagogy, and relate it to teaching and learning chemistry. As the term *feminist* has been known to evoke a variety of reactions from scientists (some of them unfriendly[1]), we begin by offering the reader a rationale for the study of feminist pedagogy:

- It describes teaching practices that can benefit *all* of our students;

- It offers ways to make science classrooms more inclusive of women; and

- It provides frameworks to help us theorize our current teaching practices.

Furthermore, a knowledge of feminist pedagogy can:

- help us build "two-way streets"[2] with colleagues from women's studies programs and

- allow us to bring an informed voice to the national and international conversations on gender and the sciences.

In short, feminist pedagogy can benefit both teachers and their students.

We begin by offering brief descriptions of the terms sex, gender, feminism, pedagogy, and feminist pedagogy. Next, a set of themes common to feminist pedagogies is outlined. The article concludes with practical suggestions and examples for those who teach.

Terminology

THE TERMS *GENDER* AND *sex* underlie any discussion concerning women and men. Sex usually refers to the biological category of male and female. While our culture recognizes only two sexes, some individuals are born "intersexed" (estimated as high as 2 percent of the population at birth) and are forced, often surgically, to adopt one of these two choices. Gender refers to the social meaning that we give to sex. For example, women may be viewed as caretakers with verbal skills and men as providers with mathematical ability. These associations represent our culture's construction of gender. Thus, our culture reduces the immense variation in human sexuality to two sexes with corresponding gender roles. While not all men and women ascribe to these, they nonetheless set the tone in our culture and engender stereotypes that can shape and define our classrooms if we do not actively intervene.

While these are simplistic definitions of sex and gender, over the last two decades the field of women's studies has come to view gender as a variable deeply embedded in the networks of human social and political relations. Gender is inextricably interconnected with other axes of social analyses such as ethnicity, race, class, sexuality, and nationality. Today, women's studies is a rich and diverse field with its own theories and debates on many subjects, including gender.

The term *feminism* refers both to movements and theories. To explain the term, we sought the collective wisdom of those gathered at a national institute for Women in Science. Feminism, the group said, promotes the social, political and economic equality—but not the sameness—of men and women. "Any decent person should be a feminist," added an engineer, explaining that feminism actively rejects patterns of superiority for men. A women's studies colleague quoted a bumper sticker, "Feminism is the radical notion that women are people," For an excellent historical overview of feminism in the U.S., see Sheila Tobias's recent book, *The Faces of Feminism* or the collection *Modern Feminisms,* edited by Maggie Humm.

Pedagogy refers to the way we teach. We may lecture, perhaps standing behind a podium. We may encourage student input and utilize it to modify course content. We may seek to involve those who remain silent during class discussions. We may provide resources to help students answer their own questions. Depending on one's pedagogy, these may or may not be our classroom practices.

Feminist and alternative pedagogies are theories "about the teaching/learning process that guide our choice of classroom practices by providing criteria to evaluate specific educational strategies and techniques in terms of the desired course goals or outcomes" (Shrewsbury 1993). They were conceived as a rethinking of traditional ways of teaching in which teachers are active and students are passive. Alternative pedagogies stem from many sources: the women's movement, the progressive educational theory of John Dewey, theories of collaborative learning, and the revolutionary pedagogy of Paolo Friere (Maher and Tetreault 1992; Sandler, Silverberg, and Hall 1996; Freire 1970). For a more complete discussion of alternative pedagogies, see *Educating the Majority* (Pearson, Shavlik, and Touchton 1989).

While feminist pedagogy shares its roots with alternative pedagogies, it is distinct in its focus on women and their experiences both in and out of the classroom. As articulated at a recent conference at the University of Saskatchewan in 1995, the goals of feminist pedagogy are to create a more hospitable place for all students, especially women, by teaching in ways that:

- acknowledge women's experience and treat them as normal

- use feminist principles in the classroom, and use them to inform the content

- empower students

- reject "open and pour" method of teaching

- insist that learning is more than memorizing content

- emphasize that learning skills such as critical analysis can be applied to all disciplines and experiences inside and outside of the classroom

- connect students' lives to content of their discipline

- seek to include rather than to exclude students and their experiences

- strive to make knowledge part of a student's world, not separate from it.

Feminist pedagogy continues to shape and is shaped by movements for alternative critical pedagogies. The search for alternatives continues today: "Feminist pedagogy is still defining itself through a process of questioning beliefs and practices in education"(Brown 1992).

Themes Common to Feminist Pedagogies

AT THE OUTSET, WE wish to stress that feminist pedagogies are *not* about easier courses, less rigorous material, or better course evaluations. Neither do they call for classrooms that are indiscriminately student-driven or a place where "anything goes." Instead, feminist and alternative pedagogies enhance the ability to use our individual ways of teaching to promote student interest and learning. The rapidly growing literature of feminist pedagogies speaks both to *what* is taught and *how* it is taught. Here we offer a description of several themes common to feminist pedagogies: a focus on women/gender, authority, position, empowerment, voice, and non-neutrality.

Feminist pedagogy focuses on *women/gender* by using teaching practices that incorporate examples from women's lives, acknowledge the history of women's accomplishments, and treat women's lived experiences as normal. Feminist pedagogy stresses an awareness of how gender relations of unequal power are inscribed in speech patterns, language, and interactions. Identifying these and interrupting them is crucial to classroom culture and climate, broadens students' understandings, and sensitizes students to the classroom dynamics that favor one group over another. This focus on gender sets feminist pedagogy apart from other efforts to transform education in a more democratic direction. A college in women's studies notes, "Just as women's liberation emerged out of women's experience within male-dominated radical political movement, gender oppression and is likely to reproduce it within the 'reformed' classroom" (contribution by Johanna Brenner, Portland State University, to a national list server on feminist pedagogy).

Authority can arise from a variety of sources. Teachers traditionally are viewed as authorities by virtue of their expertise in a particular field. As they impart knowledge, a hierarchical relationship arises between them and their students. In contrast, feminist scholarship acknowledges and develops the authority in others (especially students) and views knowledge as constructed and culture-bound. Fostering multiple authorities allows different classroom dynamics and voices to emerge. Authority shifts to students when they can interact and ask questions, where their feedback is actively sought and incorporated, and when faculty work to make themselves less intimidating and more approachable. In part, faculty give up authority through techniques such as collaborative learning and peer teaching. In turn, students gain multiple mechanisms to learn and engage the material. Authority also is reflected in the arrangement of our teaching spaces. A teacher standing behind a podium conveys a different message from one in close proximity to her students.

110

A person is always *positioned* within and across different contexts. For example, any chemist is positioned within the tradition of chemistry, which is characterized by questions, methods, and methodologies specific to the discipline. Positions are always relational: a person positioned at the margins (e.g., as a female) is marginal only with respect to the center. A person's position is also multiple and negotiated (i.e., being both parent and scientist). Never outside a particular tradition, our perspectives are always shaped by social, cultural, and historical contexts.

In academia, faculty position themselves in disciplines, which in turn are positioned in departments. Disciplinary lines are so woven into the culture of academia that their centrality may be invisible and unchallenged. The authors of *The Feminist Classroom* (Maher and Tetreault 1994) argue this lack of awareness is no accident: "Positional understandings are discouraged or blocked in academic environments." As long as disciplines are the established ways of structuring and transmitting scientific knowledge, those who conceive of knowledge differently occupy lesser positions. Areas such as women's studies or science education may become positioned at the margins of traditional disciplines. A reexamination of our disciplinary boxes and how they affect the learning process is part of a feminist analysis.

Position matters in the classroom. The specific knowledge that emerges through questions and interactions will vary depending on the positions of those engaged in the learning process. As we teach, feminist pedagogy calls us to a meta-knowledge of our position and to a recognition that our students may come from or have a different position. Those who teach need to seek a fluidity of position that shifts easily to meet the needs of different situations.

Empowerment of students is crucial. They need to become strong learners, tap their own resources, and utilize their own strengths. Feminist pedagogy de-emphasizes the role of teacher as mentor, encouraging students to become their own mentors (Brown 1992). Empowering students is thus similar to promoting active student learning. Students will miss opportunities to become independent learners if science is taught only as a set of truths. Science needs to be taught as a process, one where the experiments and data can be examined critically. Students need to contend with the changing nature of scientific knowledge and how it shapes our understanding of the world.

Feminist pedagogy calls students to find or fashion their *voice* in the classroom. They need to emerge into public space, speak for themselves, and bring their own questions to the material. Their view of the world is legitimate, and their perspective matters. The authors of *The Feminist Classroom* comment, "We have seen how the voices of women and men, of white students and students of color, of those of different ages and sexual preferences, may intersect in the construction of new and multidimensional forms of knowledge" (Maher and Tetreault 1994).

Students find their voice most naturally when the material they are studying is relevant and connected to their lives. For example, if the concept of "isotopes" is taught in the context of the diagnosis and treatment of cancer, students may be able to contribute from their personal experiences.

Another theme of feminist pedagogies is *non-neutrality of education*. In the introduction to Paolo Freire's classic work (1970), *Pedagogy of the Oppressed,* the editor notes:

> There is no such thing as a *neutral* educational process. Education either functions as an instrument which is used to facilitate the integration of the younger generation into the logic of the present system and bring about conformity to it, *or* it becomes 'the practice of freedom,' the means by which men and women deal critically and creatively with reality and discover how to participate in the transformation of their world.

Feminist pedagogy springs from these roots and challenges any claims that knowledge is value-free. Feminist classrooms explore the origins of ideas and theories, the *position* of those who put them forth, and the factors that influence how knowledge came to exist in its present forms. For example, the concept of the "laws of nature" could be examined, pointing out how "law" is a human construct to which nature may not always subscribe.

While feminist pedagogy was conceived and developed to empower and include women as equal participants in the classroom, many of its strategies undoubtedly will help all students or appear to be just "good teaching practices." As should be evident, the themes that underlie feminist pedagogy are neither new nor unique. Taken together, however, they can contribute to our theory and practice of teaching.

Useful Ideas For the Chemistry Classroom

IT WOULD RUN COUNTER to the spirit of feminist pedagogy to prescribe a set of directions that one could simply implement step by step. Accordingly, here we offer ideas that can be adapted to one's own teaching style, students, and institutional constraints. They are grouped under headings that correspond to the pedagogical themes described previously. The theme, "focus on women/gender" is omitted as a heading, as it is woven throughout. We caution against implementing an idea or two in a piecemeal fashion. These ideas can be expected to work best when they are part of a larger vision for the learning process.

General Ideas. Match your syllabus to your pedagogy.

Check the tone of the documents that you hand out or place on computer. To communicate his pedagogy, a colleague wrote in his syllabus, "I can point out the interesting sights along the way and suggest those scenic overlooks where it is worth spending more time. In the end, however, it will be up to you to construct the movie from these snapshots—you will devise your own ways of knowing"(Syllabus of Earl Peace, University of Wisconsin-Madison, chemistry department). Also cite institutional policies on sexual harassment, discrimination, and consensual relations. These can underscore your intention to have a respectful and friendly climate for all.

Match your classroom behavior to your pedagogy.

Find ways to check your classroom practices, such as by inviting a colleague to observe them. How do you respond to students? Do you attend mostly to one type, such as vocal males? Do you pose few or many questions? How long do you wait after you pose a question? Do you allow time or structure activities for students to pose their own questions? Both female and male colleagues have reported that they have been surprised at their tendencies to favor male students, and have taken steps (such as consciously alternating between male and female students) to compensate for this. A useful list of behaviors and gestures to monitor can be found in a recent ASHE-ERIC Report (Chliwniak 1997).

Consider all-female groupings within a larger class.

These are possible both on a small scale (e.g., laboratory partners or "study buddies") and on a larger scale (e.g., women in a residence hall). Based on the latter model, a program was initiated in 1996 at one of our institutions. Seventy women majoring in science or engineering participated in a residential program directed by a faculty member from women's studies (Allen). These students were given the option of enrolling in an all-female section of a larger general chemistry lecture. Students who selected this option reported more equitable "hands on" time in the laboratory and the absence of peer pressure that they felt kept them from participating in the presence of men. Collectively, they also achieved a higher grade point average than the class as a whole. Although there can be problems with this model (e.g., other sections are left with fewer women), all female groupings still merit attention. An excellent review of single-sex environments can be found in *Re-Engineering Female Friendly Science* (Rosser 1997).

Utilize resources for active learning that have been successful in creating friendly classroom environments.

For example, problem-based learning (PBL) has been cited as embodying the pedagogical suggestions of feminist authors (Armabula-Greenfield 1995).

Pay attention to group dynamics.

Although small group learning has a significant and positive effect on achievement, persistence, and attitudes towards learning for all students (Springer, Stanne, and Donovan 1998), it does not always work well. When women are outnumbered, end up in the less active roles in the group, or experience unfavorable power dynamics, small groups may work to their detriment. When dividing a class into groups, pay attention to group size, membership, roles and leadership, student resistance, and the interaction of gender with each of these parameters (Rosser 1997).

Ideas relating to authority.

Reorganize your teaching spaces. Decrease environmental cues that set you apart as an expert and any barriers to conversation. Create settings that allow student interaction and collaboration. *Structures for Science,* a handbook developed by Project Kaleidoscope (Narum 1995), contains excellent suggestions.

Be alert as you increasingly share authority with students.

Difficulties can arise, especially when female faculty attempt to reduce their "expert status" in the eyes of students. Women have reported that they have needed to be "in charge" and decisive at the outset in order to gain the respect of their students. Changes in authority need not occur quickly and can evolve naturally over time.

Recognize the different forms of student authority.

Women who return to the work force may bring life experiences that are rich in practical applications of chemistry (e.g., organic gardening, family medicine). Students who are studying agriculture or engineering may have a working knowledge of chemical issues in another field. Students who have grown up on a farm or an inner city may have unique perspectives to offer on environmental issues.

Ideas relating to voice. If you teach classes with high enrollments, find mechanisms for students to easily express themselves.

For example, you could institute a class "Board of Directors."[3] Have students select board members from their discussion sections to meet weekly with you. Monitor the dynamics of the board (as you would any group) to insure that women are repre-sented and that members do not assume stereotypic roles (i.e., women as "recorders"). In the experience of one of us, student feedback was strongly positive and the board members had opportunities to develop skills (e.g., creating a Web page for the Board: genchem.chem.wisc.edu/courses/fall97/108/middle.htm). Some representative comments from student board members are shown below ("General Chemistry," University of Wisconsin-Madison, Fall 1996; 150 students, seven board members):

- So often the voices of students are ignored. Thank you for allowing us to have an opinion that is heard.

- By having a Board of Directors, students do not have to worry about being shy.

- It gives the students a voice in some of the decisions, which is good, because sometimes professors inadvertently are unaware of what's up with the students.

- It kind of joins us all together and makes it really easy to touch base with each other.

- I think the board of directors are doing a great job. They have come up with a lot of good ideas that have been put into action right away.

- My experience in too many classes is that the professor really makes no effort to hear or communicate with their students. Thank you for making an effort.

Find creative uses for electronic mail.
    Although e-mail may sound like a minor change, its effect on communication can be substantial. One female chemistry student commented, "With email, it is much easier to talk to the instructor of a course. It also makes [talking] less threatening." Electronic mail is an alternative for students who at first may be uncomfortable approaching an instruc-tor. "Chat rooms" and list servers also provide useful avenues for students to communi-cate with each other and share their ideas or projects. Students, upon discovering that their instructor responds quickly and cordially, may begin participating in the course to a much greater extent. In fact, they may become so comfortable with electronic mail that their instructors (who at first welcomed the chance to more effectively reach their quiet or reserved students) may find themselves overwhelmed with messages. Give thought to how you can best maximize its benefits and minimize its hassles.

Teach yourself to ask, "Whose voice is missing?"
    When you hand out course evaluations, you may miss the voices of students who dropped the course. When you serve on a committee, there may be no women or peo-

ple of color present. There may be no books on women in science in the library. Handicapped restrooms may not be available. Hallways and textbooks may contain artwork and photographs of men, but few of women. People who are representative of a "missing voice" can aid others in developing a sensitivity to who or what is missing.

Ideas relating to non-neutrality and position. Find ways to smoothly integrate historical perspectives on chemical ideas and to reveal historical roots.

For a thoughtful historical analysis, see David Knight's *Ideas in Chemistry* (1992), where he casts chemistry as "the science with a glorious future behind it" and poses some unconventional questions. Connect chemistry to real people and relate the stories of individual women. As appropriate, you may wish to raise questions about the positions from which women entered the field of chemistry and the positions to which they sometimes were pushed—for example, into neighboring fields such as pharmacology or food science. Their work in supporting roles may have rendered their contributions invisible.

Discuss how both the content and practices of science reflect social and cultural biases toward what is worth knowing.

For example, utilize the questions, "Science for whom? Science by whom?" provided by Sandra Harding, a philosopher who has written extensively about gender, race, and science. Discuss also what has and has not been the driving force behind scientific knowledge in the United States:

> It would be useful to consider and study how scientific and technological priorities and representations of nature might change if women were to direct national health institutes, environmental regulatory agencies, regional agricultural policy, projects to eradicate poverty, and generally, if they were more represented in policy making in governments, science, and multinational corporations. (Harding and McGregor 1996)

Some questions go unanswered because no researchers had interest or funding. Others are answered because of external pressures, such as the military. To the extent that women and men have different priorities, they will ask different questions. A recent article on engineering students contrasts male and female priorities about global science and engineering problems (LeGrange, Rochford, and Sass 1996).

Ideas relating to empowerment. As you teach, find opportunities to examine the models of science.

Students should recognize both what is gained and what is lost when we simplify systems. They should understand the ramifications of isolating a biologically active

116

compound from its environmental matrix. They should appreciate that computer simulations can both aid and blind us. They should find out what is lost when we look at the parts, rather than the whole. Actively pursue lines of thinking such as these in order to demystify science and to empower students to think for themselves.

Students are empowered when they can raise and answer questions of their own.

Rather than solely asking for questions in class, invite questions by other mechanisms. For example, one of us assigned students to send her an e-mail message containing a chemistry question. This exercise had multiple agendas: It opened a line of communication with the instructor, emphasized the importance of asking one's own questions, and provided topics of student interest for later use in the course. Students' questions representative of those submitted to their instructor via e-mail ("General Chemistry," University of Wisconsin-Madison, Fall 1997, 170 students) are given below.

- If the atom is too small to see, then how was it possible to split it?

- Why is carbon monoxide so dangerous and how does it kill people?

- What are the philosophical problems with the science of chemistry? What, if anything, do chemists not agree on?

- How do lava lamps work? Why do those blobs inside not mix with the water, or whatever the base liquid is? Is it really a type of lava, or is that just a selling point?

- I want to know what makes a certain metal, paper, or plastic recyclable and others not?

- Why wouldn't they just make all plastic, papers, etc. from recyclables and not from styrofoam?

- How is chemistry connected to weather events?

- What happens to medications after they expire? Does their chemical structure change in some way, and if so, why? Do they become toxic or simply lose their potency?

Give thought as to how you will handle questions.

Resist the temptation to immediately supply answers. Although some questions may require immediate answers (e.g., those involving safety) others can be answered less directly by supplying a journal or reference to a web site. Student questions are likely to be far-reaching, sometimes bordering on unscientific. This provides an opportunity to talk about what content "counts" as science.

Examine the questions found in textbooks.

Some simply ask for a "right answer"; others require more thoughtful analysis. After devising a solution to a complex problem, a useful question to ask is, "What are five more possible solutions?" This requires one to keep an open mind, rather than to lock onto a first answer. Repeatedly asking this question rapidly can alter one's belief system about the nature of knowledge and how it is constructed.

Examine tendencies to simplify or to seek a single, best solution.

Sheila Tobias points out that scientists bring this tendency to complex questions (such as how to reform the curriculum), even though it may be counterproductive (1992). Allow students opportunities to evaluate a variety of solutions.

Examine textbook illustrations and photographs.

Are the men shown in active roles and the women in passive ones? Are female children shown, but none who are male? Are the photographs of men and women the same size? Are the hands that hold chemical equipment male and that hold household chemicals female? Do the hands belong only to people who are Caucasian? Similarly, check the posters and artwork in your department for stereotypes.

Reserve time in your syllabus for student-selected topics.

The amount of time allotted need not be great, as the message conveyed is what counts. In a course for non-majors, it can be straightforward to respond to student interests, as most topics can illustrate important chemical principles. Even in a majors course, the benefits gained from student input can outweigh the need to "cover material."

Conclusion

FEMINIST PEDAGOGY CAN BENEFIT all students. It calls for an increase in our openness to ideas from students, a willingness to change materials or styles if these can benefit student learning, and a way to make a place for the new knowledge and connections that students can bring to a course. Taken together, the ideas of feminist pedagogy create a theoretical context in which to examine what we teach and how we teach it. These ideas are specific enough to establish an agenda that supports women, yet broad enough to allow individuals to adapt them to their own style, classroom dynamics, and individual constraints.

Feminist pedagogy also helps us better conceptualize what is meant by "all students." As Angela Calabrese Barton (1998) points out:

> Feminist theory provides an innovative lens with which to reflect on inclusiveness in science education. ... [There is] a fundamental shift in thinking in science education circles: it shifts the reform focus from deficiencies held by women or minorities to deficiencies and discriminatory practices in science and education. ... I utilize this shift in thinking to argue that feminist theory pushes against the boundaries of the conversation regarding teaching science to all student through the construct of 'liberatory education.'

Some of the challenges encountered by those both new and experienced in using feminist pedagogies, such as feminist assessment of student work and student resistance, are documented in the publication by the National Association for Women in Education (Sandler, Silverberg, and Hall 1996). To strengthen our ability to utilize feminist pedagogy, continuing dialogue is needed between those teaching in the sciences and those in women's studies. We have been involved in two national projects that promote this dialogue, as acknowledged in the final section. Empowerment is not only for our students, but also for ourselves. By asking new questions and seeking out new colleagues, we can take ownership of existing situations and view our classrooms and students in new ways.

Acknowledgments

WE WOULD LIKE TO thank the participants of the five day Institute for Women in Science, held at University of Wisconsin-Oshkosh, June 9-13, 1997, both for their contributions and for pointing out the need for such an article as this. The Institute for Women in Science was supported in part by NSF Grant #DUE-9653437 to the University of Wisconsin Women and Science Program. Lynn Hankinson Nelson, department of philosophy, Rowan University, and Johanna Brenner, women's studies, Portland State University, also provided insightful comments through their participation in a national project [*Women and Scientific Literacy: Building Two-Way Streets* funded by the National Science Foundation and] sponsored by the [Association of American] Colleges and Universities. This project is under the directorship of Caryn McTighe Musil, whose vision to bridge women's studies and science underlies this paper. We thank two of the national advisors on this project: Angela Ginorio, director of the Northwest Center for Research on Women, University of Washington and Karen Barad, women's studies, [Mt. Holyoke College], for their helpful feedback on this manuscript. Finally, we thank the students of Chemistry 108 (75 percent female) for the many ways in which they taught and inspired their teachers.

Endnotes

1   An example is provided by James Watson in the first chapter of *The Double Helix*. In regard to his colleague Rosalind Franklin he writes, "The thought could not be avoided that the best home for a feminist was in another person's lab."

2   This metaphor, together with the articulation of the compelling need to bridge the scholarship of women's studies and science, is credited to Anne Fausto-Sterling, division of biology and medicine, Brown University.

3   This idea was suggested by Judith Burstyn, department of chemistry, University of Wisconsin-Madison.

Works Cited

A better tomorrow: Transforming the classroom through feminist pedagogy. 23 February 1995. A video available from Division of Audio Visual Services, University of Saskatchewan, Saskatoon.

Allen, C. 21 May 1996. Presentation at University of Wisconsin-System Women in Science Retreat. Appleton, WI.

Arambula-Greenfield, T. 1995. *Feminist teacher,* 9: 3, 110-115.

Barton, A. C. 1998. *Feminist science education.* New York: Teachers College Press, viii.

Brenna, J. 1997-2001. From the AAC&U national listserv, a conversation on feminist pedagogy, Women's Studies, Portland State University, Portland, Oregon.

Brown, J. 1992. *Journal of General Education,* 41: 51-63.

Chliwniak, L. 1997. *Higher education leadership: Analyzing the gender gap.* Washington, DC: ERIC Clearing House on Higher Education, 29.

Freire, P. 1970. *Pedagogy of the oppressed.* New York: Seabury Press, 15.

Harding, S., and E. McGregor. 1996. In *World science report 1996*. New York: UNESCO Publishing, 303-304.

Humm, M., ed. 1992. *Modern feminisms*. New York: Columbia University Press.

Knight, D. 1992. *Ideas in chemistry: A history of the science*. New Brunswick, NJ: Rutgers University Press.

Maher, F., and M.K. Tetreault. 1994. *The feminist classroom*. NY: Basic Books, 18, 208.

LeGrange, L., K. Rochford, and A. Sass. 1996. Gender differences among engineering and business/marketing students= rankings of science and technology-related global problems. *Australian Journal of Engineering Education*, 7:1.

Maher, F., and M.K. Tetreault. 1992. *New directions for teaching and learning*. San Francisco: Jossey-Bass Publishers, 49, 57-74.

Narum, J.L., ed. 1995. *Structures for science: A handbook on planning facilities for undergraduate natural science communities*. Washington, DC: Project Kaleidoscope.

Peace, E. 1998. Syllabus for general chemistry. Dept. of Chemistry, University of Wisconsin-Madison.

Pearson, C. S, D. L. Shavlik, and J. G. Touchton eds. 1989. *Educating the majority: Women challenge tradition in higher education*. New York: Macmillan.

Rosser, S.V. 1997. *Re-engineering female friendly science*. New York: Teachers College Press, 41, 53-67.

Sandler, B.R., L.A. Silverberg, and R. M. Hall. 1996. *The chilly classroom climate: A guide to improve the education of women*. Washington, DC: National Association for Women in Education.

Springer, L., M.E. Stanne, and S. Donovan. 1999. Effects of small-group learning on undergraduates in science, mathematics, engineering, and technology: A meta-analysis. *Review of Educational Research*, 69, 1: 21-51.

Shrewsbury, C. 1993. *Women's Studies Quarterly*, 21: 3-4, 8-16.

Tobias, S. 1997. *The faces of feminism*. Boulder, CO: Westview Press.

_____. 1992. *Revitalizing undergraduate science: Why some things work and most don't*, Tucson, AZ: Research Corporation, 16.

Gender and Science Across the Curriculum: Students Respond

Laura Briggs, Jennifer L. Croissant,
Marta Civil, and Sharla Fett

Introduction

WHAT DOES IT MEAN to introduce issues of gender and science across the curriculum? How are students in different fields responding to these curricular transformations? This article reflects on the experiences and thinking of four faculty members teaching across disciplinary boundaries that encompass science, mathematics, engineering, women's studies, and history.

In the process of teaching and revising courses, we have learned a great deal about pedagogical strategy, incorporating new content into existing disciplinary courses, and student resistance. Coming from such divergent fields—women's studies, history, mathematics, and culture, science, technology, and society (CSTS), our teaching styles, successes, and failures were diverse. However, we each were committed to moving beyond the traditional models and content dictated by our respective fields. For those of us working in the social sciences and humanities, this meant teaching students to see science, engineering, and mathematics (SEM) as a multitude of different disciplines with different approaches. We also stressed the internal heterogeneity of fields rather than presenting simple models of "Science" with a capital "S." Those of us in SEM have worked to develop complex models of what women's studies has to teach us about both the social relations of our classrooms, our fields, and the wider world. As professors, we sought to convey to our students more about each of our disciplinary assumptions. We analyze here our successes, our failures, and the obstacles we faced.

Participants in the Association of American Colleges and Universities' *Women and Scientific Literacy* project at the University of Arizona created new courses and introduced new modules or significantly modified curriculum in existing courses. Information in this article is drawn from our experiences teaching or transforming the following courses: "Women and Western Culture," "The Laboratory and Social Life of Genes," "Cultures of Biology, Medicine, Gender, and Race," "The Politics and Culture of African-American Health," "Introduction to Engineering; Women in Science and Engineering," "Technology and Society," and "Mathematics for Elementary Education Majors."

Each of us came to this project with different ideas about changing the content of our courses and especially the challenge of teaching science effectively to all students, including women students and others often underrepresented or underserved in science fields. Drawing from work in feminist as well as other radical and critical pedagogies, we did find that we had certain commitments in common—negative as well as positive. We began with the discovery that we shared an unease with how some people define "feminist pedagogy." We disliked the soft, relational version of this term suggested by the work of Carol Gilligan in *In a Different Voice* (1982, 1992) and Mary Belenky et al. in *Women's Ways of Knowing* (1986, 1997). Specifically, we were uneasy with promulgating ideas about women students' fundamental difference that some readings of Gilligan and Belenky, et al. have suggested, and rejected formulations like the following gloss of their work:

> Women seek to build connections. They seek to maintain connections that have been built. Relationships are more than a set of interactions among people. They are the web of existence. For men, the importance of separation results in the creation of rules as the web of existence. Relationships with individual people are less important than the fabric of rules. (Shrewsbury 1997)

This formulation of the pedagogical issue in terms of an absolute or even significant male-female dualism seemed unhelpful to us. We did not think women necessarily learned differently—we ourselves were women who learned quite successfully in traditional classrooms—and the identification of different learning styles as a significantly gendered one seemed to have more liabilities than benefits in the context of the work we were trying to do. It artificially homogenized women students (asserting that all women learn in the same way), while reinforcing a presumption of women students' "difference" in a context where too many instructors already have a strong belief that women's differences ought to exclude them from SEM professions and classrooms. Additionally, posing the problem in these terms, even if it seems to explain the relative absence of women in science, provided no analysis of the significant exclusion of non-elite and/or non-white men—an exclusion that historically has encompassed virtually all men from outside Europe and the United States from the doing of science. In other words, it failed to account for how the doing and learning of science became an elite, white, Euro-American male affair.[1]

124

On the positive side, we did agree that not all students—women or men—learn in the same way, nor are all students equally confident or empowered in a classroom. It was also our shared experience that teaching is a difficult job and often badly done in university settings; that intimidating students and stuffing them with "facts" is usually an ineffective pedagogical strategy, but nevertheless still a dominant one; and that instructors are also learners. Above all, what we wanted to communicate to our students was our own excitement about the possibilities of learning, thinking, and teaching across disciplinary boundaries, creating inclusive learning communities, and the ways that such composite knowledge and communities would make us all better at participating and making decisions in the complex world in which we live.

We hope that through this paper others will recognize the challenges and benefits of increasing dialogue between women's studies and the sciences, challenge intellectual and institutional barriers that still exist, and find ways to implement their own programs and practices. As we discuss and analyze our experiences in teaching across disciplinary and intellectual boundaries, we examine how students respond to different course content, the incorporation of gender literacy in science and engineering classrooms and scientific and technical literacy in women's studies classrooms, and feminist teaching techniques. Some of the tensions we experienced as we taught our courses, we believe, resulted from differing expectations among students and faculty about models of knowledge and education. These models ranged from 'fact-oriented' models of inquiry and instruction to feminist models of education and knowledge.

The incorporation of gender issues—fostering a "gender literacy" if you will—in science and engineering classrooms as well as expectations about scientific and technical literacy in women's studies classrooms took shape differently in each of our classrooms. And while some of us focused more heavily on pedagogical issues, we all realized that content changes and changes in teaching strategies are not really separable issues. The context for some of our course revisions is our university-wide general education program, which includes courses requiring a diversity component as well as general introductory work in the sciences, humanities, and social sciences. However, we also worked in this project on upper-division courses and core courses for different majors in which we tried to incorporate materials for both scientific and gender literacy.

Teaching Science In Women's Studies

LAURA BRIGGS HAS TAUGHT three introductory (100- and 200-level) courses in women's studies that have contained significant gender, science, and health components, including a new course for sophomores entitled "Cultures of Biology, Medicine, Gender and

Race," a science module in an existing "Women and Western Culture" survey course, and a freshman seminar co-taught with animal geneticist Sue DeNise called "The Laboratory and Social Life of Genes." Some of the goals for these courses have been to empower students to fear no science, to communicate an enthusiasm for the possibilities of scientific ways of knowing, and to teach tools for analyzing sexist and racist science. In these classes, we discussed the role of science in popular culture and how cultural constructions of science have reinforced notions of absolute (and hierarchically ranked) differences between men and women, people of color and whites, Euro-Americans, and the rest of the world. Perhaps most importantly, the courses worked to show how political and social organizations like the Women's Health Movement or groups like ACT UP have worked to shift scientific research priorities.

We asked students in the "Women and Western Culture" course whether they thought women's studies classes should teach content related to science. These students had no prior knowledge that the course for which they had registered would include content related to biology and medicine. In general, students were warmly positive and were persuaded that science is a women's issue. "Women's studies classes should focus on or study science because it is very important to know what is going on in the scientific world," wrote one. Another student noted that "students in these classes need to know about the kind of research and studies that are being done. They need to be able to formulate [a response] to the issues that science and research bring up, just in case the research is absurd." As this student made clear, students without a science background often feel at a loss about how to deal with scientific questions in everyday life. "As a science major and a woman, I found the two topics linked implicitly," wrote another student. She suggested further that she felt confident about her ability to negotiate the terrain of science and was working on how to frame an analysis of its social effects. "Science has become the frame for much of our cultural identity. If we don't understand how science affects culture and culture affects science, we will never truly be able to analyze, study, comprehend, or fix any part of our society." Other students wanted to formulate a feminist agenda for scientific research. "Science is not defined by the study of males. ... Science should explore women's issues," wrote one. Another commented, "Men have always controlled the field of science, [and] teaching it to women shows them how desperately they need to become involved to take control of their bodies." Many affirmed a positive contribution of the study of gender to the doing of science; one put it simply that "Science has been influenced by gender stereotypes."

A number of students also told stories of their own transformation. "Before this class, I generally believed most studies in print. But now, I know that these studies tend to be biased towards the male gender. I feel that women should be aware of this, especially in today's society. Women can't continue to wander around naively believing everything a male doctor tells them." Some of these comments reflect only an emergent inquisitiveness about science that is likely to spur a more nuanced analysis as student knowledge deepens. However, if they learned that they need not accept everything they hear just because someone said it is "scientific," they surely learned a valuable life lesson.

Women and Science in History

IN THE CONTEXT OF the history department, Sharla Fett modified a pre-existing course, "The Politics and Culture of African-American Health," a small upper-level colloquium cross-listed in Women's Studies and Africana Studies. This course examines historical problems of power and medicine in African-American history, ranging from the colonial period to the present. The aim of the revised course is to explore deeply entrenched issues of power and justice in African-American health, while at the same time rejecting a monolithic conspiratorial view of biomedical institutions. Many students entering this class with knowledge of the physical brutalities of enslavement and blatant historical injustice in medical care and public health were inclined, not without some cause, towards this monolithic view of science and medicine. A key theme of the project has been teaching about the diversity of scientific disciplines themselves, and Fett sought in this course to convey to students ways of thinking critically and subtly about the roles that biological sciences have played in U.S. racial and gender formations.

Fett focused her revisions on particular scientific fields, African-American experiences with scientific research and health care issues. She also introduced students to new theoretical scholarship on race, gender, and science. What made this course unique among the courses modified as a result of our project was the additional emphasis on African-American popular or indigenous health knowledges, such as herbalism, conjure, and southern midwifery. By taking both a topical and chronological approach, the instructor emphasized the historical contingency of both biomedicine and popular health traditions and their interactions with each other in African-American historical experiences. For example, she explored such questions as: What did the emergence of craniometry, pro-slavery ideology, and the white condemnation of enslaved women's midwifery have to do with one another? How did germ theory concepts of contagion shape the labor conditions of southern African-American laundresses in the New South? Readings and discussions explored the continuing daily relevance of medical science in past and present lives.

This course was cross-listed with Africana Studies, and included a range of students from first-year through graduating seniors, many of whom were enrolled primarily for the African-American history content, not for the analysis of gender, science, and medicine. Many students were as unaccustomed to thinking critically about Black popular health resources as they were of thinking critically about science. Thus, students found themselves challenged simultaneously along a number of lines. Several students seemed pleasantly surprised to find that African-American history could be learned in a course about science, medicine, and health, and that the science topics could capture their interest. Student-driven historical research projects on African-American health activism that made up a good portion of the students' out-of-class work helped to capture their interest. Overall, students grew in their understanding that serious considerations of science would strengthen, not dilute, the political critiques in which they were engaged.

Gender and Engineering

PERHAPS THE MOST DIFFICULT was to make significant curricular changes in courses in the field of engineering. Jennifer Croissant teaches in the college of engineering and mines, and her classrooms are filled with male students. The faculty is currently six percent female, or nine of approximately 150 faculty. The faculty and administrative approach to understanding this project has been at the level of increasing recruitment and retention of women in engineering. Rarely are issues about gender, race, class, or difference, and the implications of difference for doing or teaching engineering differently, considered in this field. Public discussion of engineering as a gendered discipline, and a system of class reproduction, heterosexuality, and contradictory race privilege is a move to a level of abstraction and critique that most engineers are neither trained to do, nor inclined toward, by temperament.

There is also extensive student resistance, by both male and female students, to critical thinking about difference and gender. As Schuster and Van Dyne point out about student resistance to women's studies content in general, women students often reject gender-focused material. One of the legacies of the women's movement is that the current generation of (traditional college-age) young women students are accustomed to thinking of themselves as "equal," and resist efforts that seem to draw attention to their "difference" (Schuster and Van Dyne 1985, 21-22). Croissant found that especially in fields like engineering, women students attempt to minimize perceived differences between themselves and their male colleagues, wishing to be understood as competent within the accepted terms of the current engineering pro-

128

fession. And, unsurprisingly, bringing up gender issues in classrooms that are over-whelmingly male is extremely difficult.

One strategy Croissant found helpful is to focus on workplace flexibility, promotion strategies, engineering ethics, and general notions of the social responsibility of professionals. Issues of gender can be introduced under these more general rubrics of understanding the profession. It is our view that feminism, in and of itself, is a delegitimated discourse in this field. In discussing gender issues in the engineering classroom, a double standard prevails. When a woman brings up gender issues, gender issues are her "special" interest or bias. When presented in "neutral" terms, or by male faculty, gender can be considered a legitimate interest of the engineering profession, but usually in terms of efficiency and opportunity. Changing course content was easier or harder depending in part on how successfully a course was organized around explicitly neutral content (however implicitly gendered). So, for example, in the context of "Introduction to Engineering," the kinds of material that could be introduced were limited to fairly neutral material on promotion and social responsibility in the workplace. Spending time on gender and professionalism would have seemed to put students at a competitive disadvantage in terms of assessment; students are assessed on their understanding of the design process, equations, methods, and technical principles. In contrast, other courses were explicitly about gender, such as the first year colloquium, "Women in Science and Engineering." That class was usually 70 percent female (with eight to fifteen students), and it was clear that the higher the number of male students who were present, the less likely women students would be to want to discuss their experience and the contradiction they felt about being young, female SEM students.

In the general education course, "Technology and Society," Croissant introduced gender issues in a number of places in the course: women and domestic labor, technological change and work displacement for women, technology and identity, and the symbolic or cultural dimensions of gender. Gender issues also appeared informally in discussion of the effects of technology on different groups of people (in this area, issues of race and class also emerged prominently). Because these materials were presented within a larger context of critical inquiry about who benefits and who bears the costs of scientific and technological change, gender issues are one dimension of variation and generally not resisted or remarked upon as particularly ideologically motivated by feminism. The lesson here is that when gender issues are presented as a matter of course—as one of the things that people in universities are supposed to talk about in general, and important to understanding the social effects of technology in particular—one faces less student resistance to feminist ideas or scholarship.

Gender and Mathematics

MARTA CIVIL, A MATHEMATICS educator, primarily teaches mathematics content courses for prospective and practicing teachers. Civil's teaching has also included mathematics courses for business majors, and recently, a mathematics course for liberal arts
majors that is a general education requirement for students who, for the most part,
do not want to take any mathematics courses. For more than ten years, Civil has
been using teaching strategies that share with feminist pedagogical theories' many
founding principles (Becker 1995; Jacobs 1994; Shulman 1994; Solar 1995). In trying to avoid framing the situation as one of a dualism between men and women—
falling into simple generalizations such as, "female students learn better in cooperative learning environments," these theories and strategies offer alternative points of
view. For example, Damarin (1990) reflects on the nature of mathematical discourse
in the classroom. She notes that in talking about "doing" mathematics, we tend to
use expressions such as "attacking a problem"—expressions that convey a notion of
aggressiveness. When talking about mathematics as a finished product, we tend to
use more "feminine" expressions, such as "elegant proofs." She then proceeds to
suggest how we can modify some of this language that helps to define the field.

For Civil, interest in changing the way that mathematics is usually taught grows
out of listening to students construct meaning in mathematics. She argues that to
enter students' mathematical worlds, instructors have to develop learning environments in which their ideas are not only heard but become part of the discussion.
When working with ethnic minority and/or working-class school children, Civil
realized the power of giving students a voice. Questions arose about whose knowledge was being represented and valued in traditional courses. These insights led Civil
to the field of ethnomathematics—a field that explores "mathematics which is practiced among identifiable cultural groups, such as national-tribal societies, labor
groups, children of a certain age bracket, professional classes, and so on"
(D'Ambrosio 1985). The notion that mathematics is neither culture-free nor value-
free is addressed by several researchers (Bishop 1991; Harris 1991; Powell and
Frankenstein 1997) and echoes some of the insights of feminist science studies that
locate hidden particularities in theories that purport to be universal.

What are the implications of all of this for everyday teaching? These theories
have helped Civil to examine what is traditionally taught in her field and how that
content is taught. For example, in transformed mathmatics courses, instructors
might provide examples of very intricate geometric patterns developed by "ethnic
minority" groups, or by women (or both) for decorating pottery or baskets or in

130

weaving (Gerdes 1995; Harris 1997). These examples, although mathematically rich, are rarely the ones chosen to illustrate, for example, concepts of symmetry in typical mathematics textbooks.

In mathematics education, the truth is that most students come with a view that in these classes one is shown how to do things and one reproduces that knowledge to pass the course. Civil developed situations in which these views were explicitly discussed. Another approach she takes is to develop a supportive environment in which all students feel encouraged to participate, and students share with everybody their "right" and "wrong" approaches to a problem. This becomes an opportunity to discuss knowledge construction. Group dynamics are also areas for potential course revisions. Regardless of the field, this is perhaps one of the hardest things faced in everyday teaching. It requires constant attention to make sure that groups are supportive of all ideas and that no one takes over or is left out.

When Civil started moving away from lecturing and showing students how to do things to having them discuss problems in small groups and present their own methods and ideas, there was some resistance. Listening to her former students as they verbalized their concerns was instructive. For example, several years ago, in a mathematics course for prospective elementary teachers, after a few days of class, one student, Donna [a pseudonym], said "I get out very frustrated from this class; like I do not get anything." It was apparent that, like many students in these mathematics courses, Donna wanted formulas to solve all the problems. She was asked, "Would you feel better if I gave you the formulas and told you to plug in numbers to get the answer?" she answered, "Yes," and explained, "because I would feel I have achieved something; at least I've got an answer." This example shows the importance of addressing students' beliefs about what it means to learn and to do mathematics. Students' sharing different methods of solving problems is challenging in mathematics, because for years they have internalized the idea that there is only one way to do any mathematics problem. Even when there are many different ways, there is one that is "better," "superior," more "efficient," and so on. Discussing different methods allows the class to engage in a conversation about what knowledge is and how it is acquired and transmitted.

Interestingly, Donna had written in her mathematical autobiography on her experience as a foreign college student in England. While there, she had observed discovery-based teaching at a local school in which young children were to create crystal shapes with minimal prior instruction. She writes, "To my surprise, the shapes that the children created were brilliant! I like the idea of children learning from other children and this experience was a fantastic demonstration of that idea." She embraced the discovery approach to learning when she saw it working for these children, but she was still not happy when it was applied to herself as a learner. As students reflect on different aspects of the course and on their experiences as mathematics learners (and in many cases, as future teachers), Civil gathered a more complete picture of their expectations and was able to have more meaningful exchanges with them.

From that same course, there were two other illustrative comments from students. One echoes the liberatory feeling that many students experience once their own ways of thinking are supported and validated. Vicky remarked in her journal, "I had fun today... There is hope yet when I can legally use my methods to solve a problem." Another student, Carol commented, "I think this discovery math technique is an absolute bunch of BS. What happens in the group dynamics is that those who understand, have background knowledge, etc., get better and people like myself get worse. I think it's a lot to ask of myself and kids, very young ones, socially to appear as a constant failure to his/herself, peers, the teacher. This class is a waste of my time, a bunch of crap, and only a lazy teacher would subject her children to it."

Vicky and Carol offer two very sharply contrasting views on their experiences in the course. In many respects, they seem to have had similar experiences when they started the journey. They both were older than the "traditional" undergraduate student in this kind of course; they both had a similar background in mathematics; and they both wrote in the mathematical autobiography about having had very bad experiences as learners of mathematics and about being terrified of mathematics. Carol's autobiography was more charged with negative feelings "The verbal abuse at being called a dummy and punished for being stupid caused me to turn off to math and just stop learning it." They both wrote, though, that they wanted to overcome this fear, that they wanted to relearn the math they had never learned. Yet the experience in this course was very different. From the beginning, Vicky embraced the idea of working with others, trying different approaches to solving problems, and experiencing the joy of solving problems: "Worked on the dollar change problem until I was tired. My problem is I can't let it go and it frustrates me to no end that it takes me so long to see things...AHA! Saturday morning and I've got it. Finally landed an easy method doing the change for the dollar problem" (Vicky's journal). Carol, on the other hand, made it clear from the beginning that she did not want to work in groups because she knew much less than the others. She was told that she could choose what worked best for her, in groups, or by herself. She usually sat with one group but worked mostly by herself and would ask questions of her peers once in a while. Carol was a graduate student in education, so she had some familiarity with the different theories on learning. From the beginning of the course, she labeled it as following the discovery approach, which she felt was not consonant with her learning style; "I guess my cognitive style is in severe clash with instruction in this course."

For Civil, it was clear that it is in the teaching approaches rather than content where changes could occur most productively in her field. Allowing students to access the mathematics being discussed and allowing everybody's ideas to be represented in class discussions were major issues that guided everyday practice. She encouraged different solution strategies, small group discussions around problems, and writing about mathematics and math learning. In the mathematics classroom, the goal is to develop a sense of a community of learners, and to make this pedagogical approach very explicit from day one. Making her teaching strategies explicit helped to minimize the instances of rejection that some students may have had towards a pedagogical approach in which they were expected to devise their own methods to approaching problems, rather than having the instructor always showing them the appropriate approaches. In recent years, Civil has made this pedagogical approach more explicit in a number of ways. For example, she begins the course by having students reading and responding to a one-page essay she wrote on "Developing a Learning Community." She uses the mathematics autobiography that each student writes at the beginning of the year as a means to start a personal dialogue with each student. This dialogue is maintained through the semester through the several journal entries students write. When issues come up in the learning community (and they do—mostly related to group dynamics and not giving everybody a voice), Civil presents these issues to the whole class and encourages feedback either in class or in writing. The easy access to e-mail has also made a difference, and Civil has noted an increase every semester in students using this medium to express their concerns about the course.

Students Respond

> Students do not always enjoy studying with me. Often, they find my courses
> challenge them in ways that are deeply unsettling. (hooks 1994)

IN TERMS OF STUDENT response, teaching science in women's studies classes was almost certainly easier, in our experience, than introducing gender issues into traditional science courses. Most students do not come to women's studies with a strong sense of what the course is "supposed" to be about. Furthermore, it was easier to add content from a "high status" area such as science to a "low status" or "soft" field such as women's studies. Some students, however, have a strong sense of what women's studies is or ought to be and do object. One women's studies major complained that "Cultures of Biology, Medicine, Gender, and Race" was not "really" a women's studies course because it had too much science in it. Others thought some science was all right, but complained about reading "heavy science" articles. Others worried about what they were missing—the "real" content of women's studies. "Women's studies classes should include science, but not put so much focus on it. The reason being, there is so much to consider about science, so many aspects, that to concentrate on it would take away from the woman part of the class." Another—in a course where one-third of the syllabus was devoted to a close reading of Toni Morrison's *The Bluest Eyes*—suggested that while a little science was a good thing, too much science meant the course did not address the "important" women's studies topics: "I would enjoy reading some literary books by women authors too."

Student resistance to science studies and feminist pedagogy, although sometimes painful, can be productive, especially when extended discussion allows students to hear and react to each other's views. For Fett, students' willingness to question new approaches helped to jump-start discussions in her African-American health class, adding elements of curiosity, excitement, and dissent. Resistance, in other words, contained within itself transformative pedagogical potential. For example, some participants balked at the introduction of the concept of the social construction of race and gender. Claiming the "obviousness" of racial differences, some students protested what they perceived as the erasure of empirical "facts" of physical difference. Interestingly, one student appealed to scientific "proof" of male-female brain structures and hormonal differences to argue that some biological differences are indisputable, thus suggesting that the race-gender analogy discussed by Nancy Stepan (1990) lives on at least in popular perceptions. Other students protested that feminist critical studies of health made science the villain in a morality play. Still others defended the importance of understanding the social uses of scientific "facts." In this context, initial resistance to an idea led to elaboration and clarification of arguments and a passionate discussion among many of the class participants.

Most intriguing, the largest number of students resisted a structural/cultural critique of institutionalized racism in science, preferring instead a racist conspiratorial theory of medical abuse. This may not be surprising, however, given the prominence of the Tuskegee syphilis study on the landscape of African-American history. Some participants, for example, resisted a structural and cultural analysis of scientific racism,

134

such as that advanced by Stephen J. Gould (1996) on antebellum craniometry. They preferred to see individual scientists consciously manipulating research results to "prove" white male superiority and maintain white male power. Individual motivation, rather than the culture of science, remained their primary concern. Analyses that emphasized social values permeating the culture of scientific study were read as "softer" critiques, somehow excusing individual action. This perception challenged Fett's own view of these critiques, since she believes they offer a more rigorous and politically incisive critique. This conflict in viewpoints remained only partially aired during the actual course. In retrospect, Fett recognizes that much fruitful discussion would have been gained from a more direct classroom exploration of theories of conspiracy and human action in the realms of race, gender, and science studies.

In her introductory engineering course, Croissant focused her changes on moving from a model of "learn these things" to a "learn how to learn" model. Because content was fixed by an associate dean of engineering, it remained largely unaffected by feminist concerns with science and technology. However, different teaching methods were implemented within the discussion sections of the course. So, as their first steps toward feminist teaching, the students were expected to know how to find, assess, integrate, and apply definitions, processes, and knowledge about very basic engineering design. Students were asked to consider their instructor more as a coach than as a teacher—to focus on process rather than rote learning. There was significant resistance to this relationship, with frustration with the lack of responsibility taken by students on the part of the instructor, and from the students' perspective, the abdication of responsibility by the teacher.[2] In course evaluations, students complained that they weren't "taught anything." In other instances, however, in part determined by student expectations and maturity, student-centered pedagogies, collaborative work, and more discursive, rather than one-way-didactic models of classroom practice were effective and received warmly by the students in engineering classrooms.

In women's studies courses, in part because of different expectations and models of learning, the discursive models of instruction were more welcomed. In the course "Cultures of Biology, Gender, Medicine, and Race" taught by Briggs, students almost universally said that they felt much more confident about their critical skills in evaluating medical and human biology research. The course changed the way they thought and acted. They reported that the course "ma[de] me be more critical of what I read and believe." They suggested that they, "learned a lot about the truth behind scientific studies of race and gender." These students did not complain about "science" per se; this course was more successful in teaching them to talk about "bad science" or "racist science" or the science of groups' inferiority. They also commented on the teaching techniques used in the class. They expressed particular satisfaction with the "discussions"—the experienced of having their own voice heard—"the way we were able to discuss everything we read." They appreciated the basic respect for all opinions in the classroom. "Things [were] taught without being really harsh toward the material/authors that were wrong." A number of students mentioned the relaxed classroom atmosphere and the presence of "humor" as a valuable part of the class. Some got the message that the point was cultural transformation. "It made me want to go out and change the world," said one. Another student suggested, "It really got me thinking about so many things, it's made me angry about the injustices in the world and makes me want to do something about it."

Similarly, students in the "Laboratory and Social Life of Genes" reported that they, too, "liked the open discussion format" and the "free discussion times." Their major assignment at the end of the semester was to spend several weeks researching the science and politics of human cloning, and to debate differing positions in assigned groups. They all agreed that this was their favorite part of the course. What is interesting about their comments is that, because the course was placed as an "enrichment" curriculum in the freshman curriculum, many of the students were there because they were floundering, some in danger of flunking out. Many admitted that they never did the assigned reading, but, following a workshop on how to find material in the library, they were all successful at finding and using material on the science and social policy associated with cloning. While the instructors found it difficult to maintain a nondirective attitude while the students developed their own way, they discovered that students learned best when they had more control.

An underlying pedagogical theme running throughout all of the courses emerging from the project is the simple proposition that students learn from each other as well as from the instructor. Fett attempted to replace the 'hub and wheel' model of classroom relations (where individual students each develop a learning relationship with the instructor) with a "network" model of the classroom as intellectual community. Whereas in previous years, students had been required to turn in papers on the week's readings at the beginning of each class, the instructor instead created a listserv and required students to post their comments on the readings to the entire class.[3] In response, students wrote with a conscious awareness of a peer audience; they referred to each other's observations, and the instructor was able to use posted comments as starting points for discussion.

Conclusion

Feminist and other new critical pedagogies require significant investment by students and a shift in responsibility often unwelcomed by them. In considering the institutional contexts that challenge female faculty, especially those in non-traditional disciplines or environments, but also those teaching unconventional subjects or with radical methods, there are many levels of challenges. Some of the tensions we experienced were a result of differing expectations about and models of knowledge and education, ranging from authoritarian "fact-oriented" models of inquiry and instruction, to feminist and co-production models of education and knowledge.

There is no one-to-one correspondence between epistemological challenges of feminist studies of science and critical classroom practices, although there are clear affinities between models of knowledge and teaching praxis. Often we expect that empowering teaching practices are associated with constructivist or critical models of knowledge. However, one can engage in student-centered, practice-based, or reflexive learning, and still have either explicit or tacit expectations for students to master certain bodies of knowledge in disciplined ways. Conversely, hierarchical, structured classroom experiences can spur students to critical thinking and an understanding of knowledge as contested. They can encourage a diverse set of interpretations of course materials. The convergence of critical thinking about knowledge in general—and science specifically—and critical pedagogies provides a very powerful instantiation of the ideas and practices of contested knowledge—a way of putting theory into practice, and under the best circumstances a reflexive opportunity for students to learn.

One of the most important messages we wanted students to hear was that science was highly relevant in their lives. The problem each of these classes analyzed involved two components—that of "science in society" and "society in science." The former encompasses the ways scientists and non-scientists use science to explain social phenomena. For example, research on racial differences in intelligence, the existence of a "gay gene," or the pre-historical basis of human male infidelity were used as examples of the important and widespread use of scientific explanations for problems of social inequality. Often, science "naturalizes" these inequalities, removing them from the realm of cultural contestation. However, such science can either be marginal or central to its field. The science of racial difference in IQ is highly contested within biology (and arguably to a lesser extent in psychology and sociology). On the other hand, the Human Genome Project, with its possibilities for naturalizing all kinds of differences, is absolutely central to the current field of molecular biology. This question of significance—and more broadly, of the kinds of scientific research that touch very little on humans at all—refers to the issue of "society in science." These courses taught students to be extremely suspicious of the deployments of "science in society," but to think with more subtlety about questions of "society in science." In other words, to say that there is "no such thing as objectivity in science," as some students concluded, was nevertheless not the end of the conversation on science, but the beginning of an exploration of how to describe scientific epistemologies. In other words, if "objectivity" is not scientific epistemology (and the scientists in the project argued vigorously that neither they nor their colleagues thought it was), then we need to figure out how to describe how scientists know what they know.

It was not our intent to experiment only with pedagogy rather than content in the mathematics teaching and engineering classrooms, but the constraints of predefined curricula (in the case of engineering) and content requirements set pragmatic limits to our amount of experimentation. In history and women's studies classes, there was more flexibility to innovate in both content and teaching style, and this led us to consider the limitations of single-course approaches to curriculum change. In addition, most of our teaching was in general education or elective offerings, reflecting and perhaps reproducing the marginality of feminist thought and practice in certain disciplines.

We believe that, as a result of these classes, students, sometimes despite themselves, take science more seriously as a cultural product and a resource for their own personal and professional lives. They also take science less seriously as a hegemonic discourse. They now question expertise and evidence in thoughtful and productive ways. The incorporation of these deeper understandings about gender and culture, and their interactions with science and knowledge, was, however, greatly resisted.

Our teaching strategies disrupted some students' sense of appropriate college-level knowledge and of teaching and learning practices. We also departed from the view of feminist pedagogies as inherently providing safe learning environments and enhancing student learning. Because of choices about process and epistemology informed by feminist science studies, our classrooms were sometimes sites of contestation. As conflicts emerge, however, they can be productive and transformative for students and faculty as we reflect on knowledge production at various levels.

This project, in retrospect, seems to be a reinvention of the liberal arts in its most progressive modes. Valuing the traditions of open inquiry, diverse perspectives, and collegial discourse, we experience the pedagogical power of liberal inquiry as applied to and combined with what we see as the best of science. We have tried to develop in ourselves and our students a way of understanding science as a useful product of society, but without dogmatic approaches to proof, credibility, objectivity, fact, and expertise. The emerging understanding of those as contingent terms, with historical specificity, is one of the greatest strengths of feminist science studies and one of the most useful resources for coherent critical pedagogies in teaching about gender, science, and society.

Endnotes

1   These have been the two main critiques of Belenky et al. and Gilligan: that their work essentializes difference and that it makes "woman" a coherent category in ways that make it hard to think race and colonialism, unless by analogy (i.e., men of color become like women, etc.). This is a substantial literature. See e.g., Harding (1996); Patai and Koertge (1994); Schniedwind and Maher (1987); Maher and Tetreault (1994). This debate about pedagogy is embedded in a larger discussion within feminist theory about what is (usually critically) referred to as "cultural feminism." See Alcoff (1988).

2   As many have noted, stereotypical models of femininity do not carry authority, so for female faculty who act in ways conventionally understood to command respect, they break gender norms for nurturance and warmth. Similarly, if speaking in "a different voice," or engaging in radical or non-authoritarian pedagogies, they may undermine their own (perhaps tenuous) claims to classroom authority or technical expertise. See for example "Resolving the Tensions" (1997) or Aisenberg and Harrington (1988). The converse apparently holds for male faculty. For enacting feminist pedagogies, see Swaffield (1996). This can lead to classroom conflict (aggressive male students), and poor teaching evaluations by peer faculty and students. See also Winocur, et al. (1989) and Goodwin and Stevens (1993).

3   New electronic technologies add to the repertoire of instructors interested in experimenting with feminist/critical pedagogy, yet need to be evaluated in the light of student responses. The predictable issues of students' differing access to computer terminals arose, although our campus is well-supplied with labs. The biggest obstacle, however, may have been busy undergraduates' patterns of course preparation, which did not allow for enough advance reading to meet the listserv posting deadlines. After some discussion well into the semester, we reached a compromise that allowed some students to continue their postings and others to follow the older model of turning work in directly to the instructor. Two lessons can be drawn from this experiment: the first that students need to be brought into discussions about technological innovations in the classroom, and the second that obstacles to new instructional models that facilitate feminist pedagogies do not always lie with the new technology, but also with older patterns of student learning.

Works Cited

Aisenberg, N., and M. Harrington. 1988. *Women of Academe: Outsiders in the Sacred Grove*. Amherst: University of Massachusetts Press.

Alcoff, L. 1988. Cultural feminism versus post-structuralism: The identity crisis in feminist theory. *Signs,* 13: 3, 405-436.

Becker, J. R. 1995. Women's ways of knowing in mathematics. In P. Rogers & G. Kaiser, eds. *Equity in mathematics education: Influences of feminism and culture.* Washington, DC: Falmer Press, 163-174.

Belenky, M. F., et al. 1986. *Women's ways of knowing: The development of self, voice, and mind*. New York: Basic Books.

Bishop, A. J. 1991. *Mathematical enculturation: A cultural perspective on mathematics education*. Boston, MA: Kluwer.

Condravy, J., E. Skirbool, and R. Taylor. 1998. Faculty perceptions of classroom gender dynamics. *Women & Language*. 21: 1, 18-27.

Damarin, S. K. 1990. Teaching mathematics: A feminist perspective. In T. J. Cooney & C. R. Hirsch, eds., *Teaching and learning mathematics in the 1990s: 1990 yearbook*. Reston, VA: National Council of Teachers of Mathematics, 144-151.

D'Ambrosio, U. 1985. Ethnomathematics and its Place in the History and Pedagogy of Mathematics. *For the Learning of Mathematics*. 5: 1, 44-48.

Fausto-Sterling, A. 1992. Building two-way streets: The case of feminism and science. *NWSA Journal*. 4: 3, 336-349.

Frankenstein, M. 1989. *Relearning mathematics: A different third R - radical mathematics*. London: Free Association Books.

Frankenstein, M. and A. Powell. 1994. Toward liberatory mathematics: Paulo Freire's epistemology and ethnomathematics. In P. L McLaren & C. Lankshear, eds., *Politics of liberation: Paths from Freire*. New York: Routledge, 74-99.

Gerdes, P. 1996. On women and geometry (education) in Southern Africa. In T. Kjergerd, K. Aasmund, & N. Linden, eds., *Numeracy, race, gender, and class: Proceedings of the third international conference on political dimensions of mathematics education*. Bergen, Norway: Casper Forlag, 207-217.

Gilligan, C. 1982. *In a different voice*. Cambridge: Harvard University Press.

Goodwin, L. D., and E.A. Stevens. 1993. The influence of gender on university faculty members' perceptions of 'good' teaching. *Journal of Higher Education*. 64: 2, 166-185.

Gould, S. J. 1996. *The mismeasure of man*. (Revised and expanded edition.). New York: Norton.

Harding, S. 1996. Gendered ways of knowing and the 'epistemological crisis' of the West. In N. Goldberger, et al., *Knowledge, difference, and power: Essays inspired by women's ways of knowing*. New York: Basic Books.

Harris, M., ed. 1991. *Schools, mathematics and work*. Washington, DC: Falmer.

Harris, M. 1997. *Common threads: Women, mathematics and work*. Staffordshire, England: Trentham Books.

hooks, b. 1994. *Teaching to transgress: Education as the practice of freedom*. New York: Routledge.

Jacobs, J.E. 1994. Feminist pedagogy and mathematics. *Zentralblatt fur didaktik der mathematik*, 26:12-17.

Maher, F., and M. K. Tetreault. 1994. *The feminist classroom*. New York: Basic Books.

Patai, D., and N. Koertge. 1994. *Professing feminism: Cautionary tales from the strange world of women's studies*. New York: Basic Books.

Powell, A. B. and M. Frankenstein eds. 1997. *Ethnomathematics: Challenging eurocentrism in mathematics education*. Albany, NY: State University of New York.

—.1997. Resolving the tensions of women faculty in the classroom. *Women in higher education*. 6:12, 7.

Ropers-Huilman, B. 1998. *Feminist teaching in theory and practice: Situating power & knowledge in poststructural classrooms*. New York: Teacher's College Press.

Schuster, M., and S. V. Dyne. 1988. *Women's place in the academy: Transforming the liberal arts curriculum*. Totowa, NJ: Rowman & Allanheld.

Schneidwind, N., and F. Maher eds. 1987. Feminist pedagogy. *Women's Studies Quarterly*, 15: 3-4.

Shrewsbury, C. 1997. What is feminist pedagogy? *Women's Studies Quarterly*, 25: 1-2, 166-74.

Shulman, B. J. 1994. Implications of feminist critiques of science for the teaching of mathematics and science. *Journal of Women and Minorities in Science and Engineering*, 1: 1-15.

Solar, C. 1995. An inclusive pedagogy in mathematics education. *Educational Studies in Mathematics*, 28: 311-333.

Stepan, N. L. 1990. Race and gender: The role of analogy in science. In D. T. Goldberg, ed. *The anatomy of racism*. Minneapolis: University of Minnesota Press, 38-57.

Swaffield, B. C. 1996. What happens when male professors enact feminist pedagogies. Presented at the 47th Annual Meeting of the Conference on College Composition and Communication. Milwaukee, WI.

Winocur, S., L. G. Schoen, and A. Sirowatka. 1989. Perceptions of male and female academics within a teaching context. *Research in Higher Education*, 30: 3, 317-329.

Conclusion

Frequently Asked Questions about Feminist Science Studies

Question One:
What is meant by "feminism," and what does it have to do with science?

Feminism has never been monolithic. In fact, it is quite common at women's studies conferences to see references to feminism that acknowledge it as a wide array of ideological, scholarly, and political viewpoints. Nonetheless, feminists share a common understanding that women have historically been devalued and denied full equality. Feminism therefore provokes questions about undeserved power differentials in society.

Feminism has influenced the production of scholarship throughout the academy, including the sciences, especially since the reemergence of the women's movement in the late sixties and the establishment of women's studies as an academic field of inquiry. Academic feminism has been rooted primarily in the humanities and social sciences, where it has sought to examine the absence of or distortions about women, document the contributions of women in many fields, and understand the mechanisms that keep subordination and marginalization in place. Such questions have deep relevance to the sciences and have been part of the emerging feminist science studies scholarship.

In addition to theorizing about women and gender, feminism has led to a tougher scrutiny of the term "universal." In social sciences, for instance, feminism has elucidated how broad theories that claim "universality" actually are more often partial, based on a white, male norm rather than a more inclusive representation of humanity. What might appear "universal" is often based on only a small portion of a population. Lawrence Kohlberg's theory of moral development, for instance, which had been constructed by observing an all male sample, has been called into question as a universal model by Carol Gilligan, who constructed a complementary model by listening to women. Gilligan's work has subsequently been questioned by Michelle Fine and others who suggest that Gilligan's model is limited as it refers to class and race. Examining such assumptions has therefore promoted constructive critical thinking in many fields, including the sciences.

Until recently, many in the sciences have been largely unengaged in feminism or feminist scholarship. Similarly, many feminists and many in women's studies have frequently ignored science or even been suspicious or critical of what was perceived as its hostility to women. Until the 1990s, very few women's studies programs included science in their curriculum. This has begun to change. Because there are now more women in science, more women teaching science, more feminist scholarship about science, and more and more of it produced by scientists, feminism and the sciences have recently embarked on an exciting period of cross-fertilization.

An example of one of the benefits of this exchange is the rich investigation into the meaning and nature of biological sex differences (female or male) and the socially constructed definitions of gender (femininity and masculinity) that vary widely across time, place, income, and race. For example, in "The Egg and the Sperm: How Science Has Constructed a Romance Based on Stereotypical Male-Female Roles" (1991), Emily Martin shows how scientists have superimposed cultural sex stereotypes inappropriately onto the process of fertilization, resulting in inaccurate descriptions of cell and molecular interactions, faulty understandings of the physiology of fertilization, and skewed research priorities. Feminist scholarship also examines ways in which ideas about sex and gender have influenced our real and imagined worlds, which Donna Haraway explores in illuminating ways in *Primate Vision: Gender, Race, and Nature in the World of Modern Sciences* (1989). In this work, Haraway investigates how scientific findings in primatology have been deeply constrained and even flawed by gendered and racialized notions. She argues, for example, that before the 1970s primatologists unwittingly imposed their gendered template on their scientific work, leading them to study only the behavior of male primates or the adult female only in a mother-child relationship. As a result, they developed an inaccurate understanding of primate behavior, lacking attention to the role of female primates, including the extent of their sexual choice, aggressiveness, or even polyandrous behavior.

In applying feminist analyses to scientific ideas and practices, feminism sees science, like all spheres of intellectual activity, as conditioned by historical circumstances, societal beliefs, and accepted norms. In this analysis, therefore, it is logical

146

that values and concepts associated with maleness and femaleness, bound as they are by time and place, would influence scientific scholarship and practice as they do other spheres of intellectual or social activity. An initial task of feminist science studies scholars has been to identify in what ways notions about gender have, in fact, influenced scientific thought and practice.

Feminist analysis has helped us understand why women have not participated fully in scientific communities and why many still feel unwelcome when they do. It also articulates the reasons why it is advantageous to science that there be a diversity of people and perspectives in the scientific community. Finally, feminist analysis helps to improve more traditional accounts of science and may contribute to substantive changes in both the culture and content of scientific practice and knowledge. By correcting distortions, feminist scholarship can lead to more accurate and less culturally limited representations of the natural world. This improved science may attract more women to the field as well as benefit those influenced by its findings.

Question Two:
What is feminist science studies, and how did it originate?

FEMINIST SCHOLARS IN THE sciences and in the history and philosophy of science have been analyzing and examining scientific theories and practices for the past fifteen to twenty years. Beginning with ground breaking works by feminist scientists like Evelyn Fox Keller, Anne Fausto-Sterling, Ruth Hubbard, and Marion Lowe, and feminist philosophers like Sandra Harding, feminist science studies is now a thriving field of scholarly activity with increasing numbers of practitioners in the U.S. and around the world. While not necessarily called "feminist science studies" in earlier periods, many of the ideas in this field, in fact, extend back into the last century of the women's movement.

Feminist science studies today and in earlier periods has brought to the study of science an awareness of the costs of excluding women and other marginalized groups from full participation in science. Part of the loss is to those excluded individuals who, because of their sex, racial-ethnic background, or class, have been deprived of the pleasures and challenges, the rewards and power, of studying and "doing" science. But society as a whole has lost out on the talents and insights that they could have brought to science and technology.

As astronomer Maria Mitchell commented in 1873, "I used to say, 'How much women need exact science,' but since I have known some workers in science who were not always true to the teachings of nature, who have loved self more than science, I have now said, 'How much science needs women.'" Mitchell's comment presages today's feminist science studies. When scientists assume that simply using the scientific method assures that their personal and cultural values are not affecting how they do science and thus what science they develop, they fail to acknowledge that their biases might affect science at all stages of development. As Helen Longino has pointed out in *Science as Social Knowledge* (1990), social and political interests, as well as personal biases, have an impact on the production of scientific knowledge. Social, political or personal interests can affect:

- how scientists set priorities for scientific investigation;

- what questions are posed about a topic;

- what explanatory framework or theory frames a scientific study;

- what methods are used;

- what data are considered valid and invalid;

- how data are interpreted;

- how data in one study are compared to data in other studies;

- what conclusions are drawn from the analysis of scientific data; and

- what recommendations are made for future studies.

That does not mean that feminist science studies argues that African-American women, for example—or Puerto Rican men or white women—necessarily look at scientific problems differently from the white men who have dominated Western science. But which problems or diseases, for example, are chosen for intensive study by a scientific community is likely to be determined by what that community knows about and what it thinks is "important." In the U.S., for example, funding for breast cancer research did not become a Congressional priority until women's health activists organized and lobbied for more funds and for a rethinking of standard scientific approaches to the problem.

Scholars in feminist science studies have pointed not only to neglected areas of scientific research but also to the uses and abuses of that research. In the same year that Maria Mitchell appealed for the inclusion of women in science, Dr. Edward Clarke published his highly influential book, *Sex in Education, or a Fair Chance for the Girls* (1873). Alarmed about women trying to gain admission to American colleges that did not admit women, or to new schools for women, like Vassar and Bryn Mawr, Clarke claimed that women would ruin their health if they went to college. Worse, they would impair their ability to bear children. The evidence for Clarke's treatise consisted of a smattering of anecdotes about a few young women whose physical or mental health suffered after attending college for a year or two.

Despite the anecdotal and incomplete nature of his evidence, Clarke's book went through multiple editions and was widely cited as scientific evidence that women should not, for their own sakes and for the sake of society, go to college. In response, Dr. Mary Putnam Jacobi, a leading female physician, did survey research of young women attending college and found no significant negative effect on their health. Even in the nineteenth century, then, a form of feminist science studies existed. It emerged from a concern for fairness and equity for women as full participants, recognized and rewarded for their contributions in all sectors of society. A more complete description of this early period of activism by women scientists and physicians can be found in Margaret Rossiter's groundbreaking study, *Women Scientists in America* (1982).

As large numbers of women gained access to colleges and universities in the 1970s, contemporary feminist science studies emerged in a new form. For the past several decades, feminist scholars have amassed convincing evidence that cultural beliefs about gender, race, and class have strongly influenced our current structures of knowledge. This scholarship developed, in fact, at the same time that other fields were being transformed by feminist ideas. Scholars inside and outside of science asked the same questions of the fields of science as their colleagues were asking in other fields like history, psychology, or literature: Where were the women in science, and how was their work valued? What was their history? How might constructing a more accurate history of science, one that takes women seriously, influence our understanding of both the history and the specific content of science? How have traditional understandings of and assumptions about gender influenced the production of scientific knowledge? How do cultural beliefs about gender affect the priorities, methods, and methodologies in the sciences?

Such an approach requires understanding science in relation to forces—political, economic, social—that shape it and the people who dominate the field. Science studies in general seeks to understand science as a human endeavor, and feminist science studies recognizes that categories of masculine and feminine—as well as other major categories of "difference"—carry meanings of differential power and status in society, affecting the sciences as they do other fields.

Feminist science studies scholars address a variety of equity issues. They are concerned not only with women and gender, but also with any group denied access, encouragement, and resources—whether inadvertently or by design. Feminist science studies is also concerned with the historical uses of science to justify inequalities. Its scholars believe that scientists and science shapers need to understand and acknowledge how science was and is involved in discrimination, so that they may break such patterns. These scholars work to eliminate current biases, teach how values enter into and shape science, and promote ideals of fairness, equity, and justice in the development of and uses of science.

Question Three:
Does feminist science studies suggest a form of relativism where all perspectives are "right"? Doesn't science need to remain objective?

PROBABLY ONE OF THE most common misconceptions about feminist science studies is that it is somehow anti-science or rejects the basic tenets of the scientific method. Scholars in the field of feminist science studies, as well as many other scholarly fields that intersect with the philosophy of science, have convincingly argued that science is not and can never be culturally neutral, and yet feminist science studies scholars have refused to reject all scientific methods or notions of objectivity. Feminist science studies simply argues that scientists do not work in a void; pure objectivity is impossible. Science defined as aperspectival and free of biases is an oversimplified and false representation of science.

Building on the groundbreaking work of Thomas Kuhn, feminist science studies scholars have argued that scientific objectivity doesn't simply rest with individual scientists. Instead, it is the result o f a consensus reached by a community of scientists working within a cultural context. The fact that communities of scientists have traditionally been comprised primarily of white men of privilege has had a profound impact on how scientific practice and understandings of objectivity have developed.

Technologies, the language of science, and research strategies are all human constructs. Scientists do not just discover laws and identify "truths." Practicing scientists construct hypotheses by examining the world, experimenting with using the tools they invent, and interpreting what they find within the context of what they know. Scientists constantly make judgments in the course of their work. They determine whether the results of an experiment or a set of data are valid, consistent with previous results and with prevailing explanatory frameworks, or spurious—the result of identifiable or unidentifiable errors. These judgments are rendered within a set of assumptions that may be influenced by cultural, scientific, and individual beliefs and values.

Does this mean that all scientific knowledge is relative? Certainly not. Feminist science studies suggests that scientific communities are *more* objective when unexamined biases are brought out into the open. Feminist scholars like Sandra Harding, Helen Longino, and many others also celebrate the utility and value of scientific endeavors.

Further, no one is arguing that what scientists have done "does not work." The ability to reproduce experiments and make predictions is highly valued, and scientists should continue to use these valuable methods of inquiry. But to embrace the value of scientific methods and "products" does not mean that one can assume all of science is free of political influences or that a scientist's desires and interests do not influence his or her work.

Scientists are engaged participants in their work. They use reason and intuition much as artists and writers do. Further, embracing the feminist science studies tenet that all knowledge is "situated" in some context should only strengthen the scientific method. In studying the natural world, for instance, any search for context dependency, for how methodological and epistemological concerns may influence how scientists construct theories and define what is knowledge, should deepen how one understands the natural world, not weaken it. Feminist scientists do not see this as a debate between objectivity and relativism. The real goal is to strive for what Sandra Harding has called "strong objectivity"—where all sources of error or bias, cultural as well as technical, are taken into account.

Question Four:
Since it is sometimes critical of existing scientific paradigms and practices, won't feminist science studies discourage women from pursuing science?

DATA SUGGEST THAT, LONG before feminist science studies existed, many women were discouraged and dissuaded from science as it was practiced and taught. Feminist science studies scholars have been part of reform efforts to reverse that trend. Rather than discouraging women from science, feminist science studies seeks to draw women to science and to foster scientific literacy. It addresses issues of access and retention of women in scientific fields by providing multiple entry points and perspectives for women and other minority groups who have been traditionally underrepresented in science fields.

Feminist science studies does, however, ask students, faculty, administrators and others—scientists and non-scientists, male and female—to rethink their foundational ideas about science. In its challenge to scientists to examine their assumptions about their work and acknowledge that societal values and beliefs affect their scientific practice, the literature of feminist science studies invites both female and male students to consider what it means to be a scientist.

Several studies indicate that while there have been dramatic gains in the numbers of undergraduate women students in science, mathematics, and engineering, the percentages of women pursuing postgraduate work declines. In 1993, women received 45 percent of all bachelors degrees in science, 36 percent of all masters degrees in science, and only 30 percent of all Ph.D.s in science and engineering fields (NSF 1996). These numbers vary significantly according to the field of science, as well, with the numbers of women in physics far lower than the numbers of women in biological sciences, for example.

In looking at the reasons for uneven or declining numbers, researchers find that female students face a variety of obstacles that keep them from pursuing careers in science fields. These obstacles include low expectations from parents and teachers, lack of self-confidence in their ability to "do" science, and overt and covert sexual harassment and discrimination by male colleagues and/or advisors. In addition, when female students find themselves one of the few women in a science class or department, the isolation can be very difficult. Also, the prospect of a lifestyle as a scientist that requires long hours and often does not make room for the possibility of having a family makes considering a career in science unattractive to many women.

To encourage women to pursue scientific majors and/or careers, the literature of feminist science studies suggests ways of practicing and thinking about science that are more inclusive and welcoming for women—and in the process often result in better science education for all students, male and female alike. Some changes advocated by feminist science studies scholars include the use of more collaborative learning, group work, and experiential education frameworks in science courses; the increasing use of scholarship on the history of science, so that women students can place science in its historical context and see why past scientific practices and ideas have discouraged women from becoming scientists; and attention to increasing the number of female mentors and faculty members in the sciences to help address climate issues for female students.

While it challenges some students' expectations about science, feminist science studies often, in fact, works to attract rather than discourage women from pursuing science careers. Feminist science studies opens up science to new viewpoints and allows women to approach scientific work in multiple ways. This, in turn, encourages women to see the rewards in studying science without requiring them to give up their gender identifications and other interests in order to succeed.

Question Five:
How can I possibly incorporate feminist science studies into my courses when I already have insufficient time to cover everything?

THE QUESTION OF CONTENT coverage has historically been hotly contested in many disciplines. In many ways this is a practical question to ask of science teachers because of an ever more rapidly growing store of scientific knowledge. It is a practical question not in the sense of "How do I do this new work in my classroom and laboratory?" but, rather "How can I use the literature of feminist science studies to help set priorities in my courses?"

Many teachers have responded to the explosion of scholarship by developing frameworks of selection and coalescence of factual material, usually moving to greater generality and to teaching some key concepts. Establishing these key concepts has always involved some level of controversy and negotiation. Those who teach science courses, particularly at the introductory level where one needs to lay the broadest foundation, feel that conceptual clarity is gained at the expense of a dream of "complete coverage."

Feminist science studies provides a thoughtful, practical, and theoretically rigorous framework—an additional set of intellectual tools—for carrying out this process of selection and synthesis. It suggests avenues for the reform of particular courses as well as the reconfiguration of departmental programs. The systematic insights of feminist science studies scholars can provide students with a broadened context for understanding key scientific concepts. This context can promote more effective learning and retention of important content. Teaching science in context can motivate students who might otherwise turn away from science. They are more motivated because they can identify avenues of connection to their own lives and develop a greater appreciation of the more general links between the sciences and their social, political, economic, and ethical contexts. This also teaches students to pose even better questions about the content in science courses.

Question Six:
What specific relevance does feminist science studies have for scholarship and teaching in the physical sciences, engineering, and mathematics?

MANY PEOPLE QUESTION THE relevance of feminist scholarship to the so-called "hard sciences." Admittedly, the connections are not always readily apparent for those who teach in disciplines such as math, engineering, and the physical sciences. However, feminist science studies does indeed have implications for both research and teaching practices in these domains. We begin here by examining feminist ideas relevant to mathematics, as its principles are employed by almost everyone who teaches in science and engineering fields.

It is commonly assumed that mathematics is culturally neutral because it deals with abstractions, presumed to be stripped of all cultural context, and therefore not culture-laden in any obvious sense. However, recent scholarship (both in feminist science studies and especially in the new field called ethno-mathematics) supports the view that culture and language influence mathematics itself and that different societies have different versions of mathematics. Feminist scholars have been arguing for at least two decades that "culture is classification." How people categorize things is one of the major differences between one culture and another. And mathematics is certainly, among other things, a system of classification.

In mathematics, problems of interest at particular historical moments have led to a particular set of methods and techniques that constitute a large part of the body of mathematical knowledge. However, these existing methods then determine the kinds of problems and applications pursued in the field. Consider the inherited methodologies that proceed by reducing the complex to the simple. Alternatively, complexity could be valued over simplicity, and we could privilege properties exhibited by whole systems over the study of individual constituents acting independently. This is not to say that feminists necessarily advocate embracing the value of complexity over simplicity; it is rather to point out that operating with different world views may lead to organizing things differently. Another example is the historical privileging of linear and hierarchical relationships in Western mathematics over non-hierarchical and non-linear ones. Consider also the fact that if set theory or differential equations are justified because they "work" for physics, using other disciplines as one's starting point might justify different mathematics, different logics.

As yet another example, consider the dominance of the ideal of a logical proof in Western mathematics. As Bonnie Shulman argues in her article, "What if We Change our Axioms?" (1996), accepting this ideal as a dominant yardstick leaves out things that elude systematic analysis and (re)organization. One observes things readily classified with known names, and overlooks or disregards everything else. Particular frameworks determine what constitutes not only an answer, but even the questions asked. As in the other scientific fields in which feminist science studies has had an impact, in an area like mathematics, feminist science scholars urge paying attention to what has not been studied—what has been left out—as well as to assessing the validity of current theories.

Feminist science studies scholars also suggest that it may be unhelpful in the pursuit of knowledge or social change to cling to a belief that one system or theory will be found to explain everything worth explaining. The world, especially as human beings influence it, seems too complicated for that. Feminist scholars in many fields have long advocated looking at things from different standpoints. At the same time, feminist science studies scholars have emphasized that the existence of multiple perspectives and starting points does not mean that all approaches are tractable or that all perspectives work equally well. Feminist science studies scholars encourage studying multiple standpoints in order to benefit from the insights that occur when one explores the ways in which different perspectives inform one other. Feminist science studies is also, nonetheless, explicit in its rejection of epistemological relativism.

Building on feminist work in other disciplines, we can teach our students to look for underlying assumptions in all scientific practices. It is also important that the mathematical and physical sciences not be presented as an unchanging body of knowledge—complete, certain, and absolute. In fact, many practicing mathematicians and scientists have a very different image of mathematics and science than does the general public. Many of them see it as a creative, intuitive, and speculative endeavor. This suggests a pedagogy that emphasizes the creative (and culturally dependent) process of actually doing science. For example, rather than merely repeating the codified and axiomatic presentation that appears in most mathematics textbooks, a pedagogy that shifts emphasis from final product to process gives the student a more accurate view of the practice of mathematics. Such approaches also have the additional benefit of being found to appeal to the minds and hearts of many previously "math anxious" students.

Those who teach mathematics, physics, chemistry, or other "hard" sciences may find it difficult to understand the relevance of social variables such as race, ethnicity, or gender to their discipline. For example, one might well ask, "What does race and ethnicity have to do with the second law of thermodynamics?" (Of course, there is nothing unique about thermodynamics; a similar question could be asked about x-rays, molecular orbitals, or the silicate rocks in the Earth's crust.) The implication of any such question is that the laws of nature are objective and free of any human bias. However, while the empirical adequacy of the law may not be in question, whether or not a given law works isn't the only substantive issue. Feminist science studies scholars are interested to know the historical and social context in which scientific laws and theories are developed. It is important for students to understand that the second law of thermodynamics is not self-evident, but evolved out of the context of the industrial revolution and, as such, is a product of that era and reflects its dominant values and the ways people were interested in interacting with the natural world.

Furthermore, as physicist and feminist science studies scholar Karen Barad points out in her article, "Agential Realism: Feminist Interventions in Understanding Scientific Practices" (1998), feminist scholarship is not limited to analyzing gender relations; rather, feminists are concerned with larger epistemological issues as well. Barad quotes Joseph Rouse who suggests that feminist approaches to science "are not simply about relations among men and women but are focused precisely on how to understand agency, body, rationality, and the boundaries between nature and culture." Indeed, feminist science studies scholars have made important contributions to scholarship about the very nature of scientific practices. They have, for example, provided empirical evidence in support of the current view that what we call "the sciences" are actually not as unified as one might think, but rather entail heterogeneous, varied, and changing sets of practices. Hence, there is no justification for presuming that the same kinds of analyses that apply in the life sciences have relevance for the physical sciences. Once again, however, this does not mean that feminists have nothing to contribute to our understanding of the physical sciences. For example, Barad's research, which uses physics as a starting point, is concerned with understanding the interaction between human and nonhuman, material and discursive, and natural and cultural factors in the production of knowledge. One of the aims of her approach is to move considerations of scientific practices beyond the well-worn traditional realism vs. social constructivism debates.

As noted above with regard to mathematics, it is important in the physical sciences to consider what is not being studied. Whose questions are we addressing when we teach science?

Which agendas are pursued and which are left untouched? What drives the topics we research? How does boxing science into the existing disciplines affect our thinking? Feminist scholarship can contribute questions such as these to the teaching of the "hard" sciences, mathematics, and engineering.

These questions also can help unleash the creativity of students who have seen no reason to study or to strive towards mastery of material that appears disconnected from their world. The pedagogical approach that many in the physical sciences use in their teaching removes the Second Law from its historical and social context, leaving behind only a group of mathematical symbols. However, the point is that this type of decontextualized teaching has gained prominence for reasons that are far from culturally neutral. The new pedagogies that seek to train students to attend to social, cultural, and political, as well as natural factors in the production of scientific knowledge can find support and a theoretical basis in the field of feminist science studies.

Works Cited

Barad, K. 1998. Agential realism: Feminist interventions in understanding scientific practices. In M. Biagioli, ed., *The science studies reader*. NY: Routledge, 1-11.

_____. 1996. Meeting the universe halfway: Realism and social constructivism without contradiction. In L. H. Nelson and J. Nelson, eds., *Feminism, science, and the philosophy of science*. Boston, MA: Kluwer Academic Publishers, 161-194.

Barton, A.C. 1998. *Feminist science education*. New York, NY: Teachers College Press.

Fausto-Sterling, A. 1985. *Myths of gender: Biological theories about women and men*. New York, NY: Basic Books.

Ginorio, A.B. 1995. *Warming the climate for women in academic science*. Washington, DC: Association of American Colleges and Universities.

Gould, S.J. 1981. *The mismeasure of man*. New York, NY: W.W. Norton.

Haraway, D. 1989. *Primate visions: Gender, race, and nature in the world of modern science*. New York, NY: Routledge, Chapman & Hall, Inc.

Harding, S.G. 1995. Can feminist thought make economics more objective? *Feminist economics*. 1:1, 7-32.

_____. 1986. *The science question in feminism*. Ithaca, NY: Cornell University Press.

Hubbard, R. 1982. *Biological woman—the convenient myth*. Cambridge, MA: Schenkman Publishing Co., Inc.

Keller, E.F. 1983. *A feeling for the organism: The life and work of Barbara McClintock*. San Francisco, CA.: W.H. Freeman and Company.

Kuhn, T. 1962. *The structure of scientific revolutions*. Chicago, IL: University of Chicago Press.

Longino, H. 1990. *Science as social knowledge: Values and objectivity in scientific inquiry*. Princeton, NJ: Princeton University Press.

Martin, E. 1991. The egg and the sperm: How science has constructed a romance based on stereotypical male-female roles. *Signs*. 16:485-501.

Musil, C.M., ed. 1989. *The courage to question: Women's studies and student learning*. Washington, DC: Association of American Colleges and Universities.

National Science Foundation. 1996. *Shaping the future: New expectations for undergraduate education in science, mathematics, engineering, and technology*. Washington, DC: National Science Foundation.

Rosser, S.V., ed. 1995. *Teaching the majority: Breaking the gender barrier in science, mathematics, and engineering*. New York, NY: Teachers College Press.

Rossiter, M. 1982. *Women scientists in America: Struggles and strategies to 1940*. Baltimore, MD: The Johns Hopkins University Press.

Shulman, B. 1996. What if we change our axioms? A feminist inquiry into the foundations of mathematics. *Configurations*. 3:427-451.

For a more extensive annotated bibliography, visit the Women and Scientific Literacy Web site at www.aacu-edu.org/Initiatives/scilit.html.

biographies

Authors' Biographies

159

Authors' Biographies

Donna Bickford

DR. DONNA BICKFORD is a full-time lecturer in women's studies at the University of Rhode Island. She is a founding member of the Literature Teaching Assistant Development Committee, a committee whose charter was the design and implementation of a program that trains teaching assistants placed in literature classrooms for the first time. Her research interests are in the connection between literature and social change, 20th century women writers of the Americas, Latin American testimonial novels, transnational comparative literary criticism, and feminist pedagogy. She has been a participant in all the events sponsored by the Women and Scientific Literacy Project.

Faye Boudreaux-Bartels

DR. FAYE BOUDREAUX-BARTELS is a professor in electrical engineering at the University of Rhode Island. She was a Fulbright Scholar in France in 1981 and recipient of Zonta International Amelia Earhart Fellowships in 1979, 1980, and 1981. She has been awarded over $700,000 in research grants from the Office of Naval Research, Navalex, and the United States Naval Underwater Systems Center, and she has written three chapters and over fifty refereed journal or conference papers. She was awarded the 1988 Senior Paper Award by the IEEE Acoustics, Speech, and Signal Processing. She has received two University of Rhode Island faculty excellence awards and was elected to serve on the IEEE/ASSP National Advisory Committee on Digital Signal Processing. For several years, she has co-organized and co-led the College of Engineering Bridge Camp for entering first year women in engineering.

Laura Briggs

DR. LAURA BRIGGS is an assistant professor in the women's studies department at the University of Arizona. She also holds a joint appointment in the department of anthropology and courtesy appointments in department of history as well as comparative cultural and literary studies program. She teaches courses on the cultural contexts of science, history of gender and science, and a graduate seminar on feminist postcolonial studies and critical race theory. Her scholarly fields include U.S. Women's History, Social and Cultural Studies of Science, and Critical Race Theory and Postcolonial Studies. She has published articles on the history of birth control in Puerto Rico and the question of Clinical Engineering Division (CED) sterilization, and is currently working on a book entitled *Reproducing Empire: Race, Sex, and Science in the U.S. Imperial Project in Puerto Rico,* that grapples with the specifically sexual and gendered content of struggles for political legitimacy in Puerto Rico. Her other research interests are eugenics and reproductive technology.

Virginia Brown

DR. VIRGINIA BROWN is a professor of psychology and director of the honors program at Rowan University. She was the leader of the Rowan grant team and in that capacity facilitated the year-long faculty development seminar on gender and science, which included bringing speakers to the campus to address women and science issues. She participated in several panel presentations that focused on gender and science studies and was also part of the three person team that developed and piloted a new interdisciplinary course "Issues in Women's Health" for the Honors program. Dr. Brown's Ph.D. is in social psychology, and her research interests include media influences on women's self-images, evaluation of women as leaders, and women's roles in global environmental change.

Marta Civil

DR. MARTA CIVIL is an associate professor of mathematics at the University of Arizona. Her research in mathematics education spreads over two areas: teacher education and equity in mathematics education. In particular, her focus is on a socio-cultural approach to the mathematics education of ethnic and language minority students (school age and adults). She is particularly interested in participatory approaches to the teaching of mathematics. Her teaching approach involves small group discussion, hands on activities, and use of technology.

Jennifer L. Croissant

DR. JENNIFER L. CROISSANT is an assistant professor of materials science and engineering, anthropology, and sociology at the University of Arizona. She earned her Ph.D. at Rensselaer Polytechnic Institute in 1994. Her current interests are pain measurement devices, narratives in and of archaeological thought, historical and sociological studies of scientific instrumentation, bodybuilding and elite athletic knowledge and use of pharmaceuticals, foods, and herbal supplements, prosthetics design and rehabilitation engineering, and cybernetics and society.

Lynne Derbyshire

DR. LYNNE DERBYSHIRE is an assistant professor of communication studies and women's studies at the University of Rhode Island. Her research interests include women and public discourse, especially nineteenth century woman's rights discourse and women and constitutive discourse. She has been at URI since 1987, and is now director of basic courses in communication studies. Teaching interests include gender and communication, contemporary rhetorical criticism, feminist theory, and diversity. She became involved in the Women and Scientific Literacy Project through her involvement in the Women's Studies Program and the Women's Equity Committee.

Bette Erickson

DR. BETTE ERICKSON is assistant director of the Instructional Development Program. In 2000-2001 she coordinated the *Faculty Fellows Program: Learning Community for Science, Mathematics, and Engineering Faculty* at the University of Rhode Island. The SMET Faculty Fellows Program brought together fifteen faculty members for a year-long, in-depth exploration of teaching and learning in SMET disciplines. SMET Faculty Fellows examined current research on teaching and learning in SMET disciplines, explored a variety of methods and approaches for engaging and retaining students, adapting and testing promising approaches in courses, and supported other participant's efforts to experiment.

Sharla Fett

DR. SHARLA FETT is an assistant professor in nineteenth-century United States history at the University of Arizona. She received her MA from Stanford University in 1988 and her Ph.D. at Rutgers University in 1995. Her expertise includes antebellum scientific racism, women as healers, African-American women and slave doctoring, and African-American midwifery in the twentieth century south.

Angela B. Ginorio

DR. ANGELA B. GINORIO is the director of the Rural Girls in Science Project, associate professor in Women Studies, and adjunct associate professor in the departments of psychology and American ethnic studies—all at the University of Washington in Seattle. She teaches courses, such as "Women and/in Science," "Issues for Ethnic Minorities and Women in Science and Engineering," "Gendered Technologies," and "Women and Violence." Her scholarship focuses on factors affecting access to and experiences in science and engineering of underrepresented groups (students and faculty of color, women, students from rural backgrounds), with particular attention to impact of socially defined identities, parental involvement, and mentoring. One of her most recent publications is "The feminist and the scientist: One and the same" (2000) with Terry Marshall and Lisa Breckenridge in *Women's Studies Quarterly.*

Lisa Harlow

DR. LISA HARLOW is professor and associate chair of psychology at the University of Rhode Island. She earned her Ph.D. at the University of California, Los Angeles with an emphasis in psychometrics and measurement. She is the director of the graduate program in experimental psychology. Her interests are in multivariate statistics and women's health. She has more than fifty scholarly publications, emphasizes attitudes and performance in "friendly science" statistics classes, multivariate models of women's health and psycho-existential functioning, and promoting diversity in learning environments. She currently mentors more than three dozen graduate and undergraduate students.

Donna Hughes

DR. DONNA M. HUGHES is a professor holding the Eleanor M. and Oscar M. Carlson Endowed chair in Women's Studies at the University of Rhode Island. Her research and writing include violence against women, sexual exploitation, and women's organized resistance to violence. She also works on issues related to women, science, and technology. Her research has been supported by the National Institute of Justice, the National Science Foundation, the Association of American Colleges and Universities, the Norwegian Agency for Development Cooperation, the International Organization for Migration, and the Council of Europe. She is the University of Rhode Island team leader for the Women and Scientific Literacy Project.

Sharon Kinsman

DR. SHARON KINSMAN received the Ph.D. in ecology and evolutionary biology from Cornell University in 1982 and currently is an associate professor of biology at Bates College. At Bates College, she has served on the program committees for women's studies and environmental studies. Recently she spent a sabbatical leave, supported by a Bates College Phillips Fellowship, as a visiting scholar in women's studies, the Southwest Institute for Research on Women, and ecology and evolutionary biology at the University of Arizona. Her areas of expertise in biology include plant reproductive biology and tropical ecology. Her current feminist science studies project examines the "foreign interference" paradigm in plant reproductive ecology. She was co-planner and co-facilitator (with Bonnie Shulman) of the first year's faculty development seminar (1997-98) "Scientists Encounter the Feminist Challenge" for the *Women and Scientific Literacy* project.

Janet Moore Lindman

DR. JANET MOORE LINDMAN is an associate professor in the history department and coordinator of the Women's Studies Program at Rowan University. As a member of the Rowan grant team, she participated in and facilitated part of the faculty development research seminar on gender and science, brought speakers to campus to talk about women and science for Women's History Month (Bonnie Spanier and Sheila Tobias), and gave presentations on the history of women and science to a summer institute for middle school girls sponsored by Rowan's School of Engineering. She was also part of a three person team that devised and taught a new course entitled "Issues in Women's Health." Her Ph.D. is in U.S. women's history and U.S. colonial history, and her research interests are gender history, religious history, and cultural studies. She has published several articles and is the co-editor of *A Centre of Wonders: The Body in Early America* (Ithaca: Cornell University Press, 2001).

Helen Mederer

DR. HELEN MEDERER is a professor of sociology and women's studies at the University of Rhode Island. Her present research is a four-year study of the impact of governmental management of the commercial fishing industry on family power and work roles in commercial fishing families. She has also studied military families and women employed by the State of Rhode Island. Other teaching and research areas are in the sociology of aging and sexual inequality. Her office was in the now-closed PCB-contaminated social science building on campus. She became involved in the Women and Scientific Literacy Project as a result of her interest in women and work environment contamination.

Catherine Middlecamp

DR. CATHERINE MIDDLECAMP is the director of the Chemistry Learning Center and a distinguished faculty associate at the University of Wisconsin-Madison. She teaches general chemistry for liberal arts students and is a co-author of *Chemistry in Context,* a project of the American Chemical Society that applies chemistry to the "real world" issues of society. She served on the national advisory board for the *Women and Scientific Literacy* Project at the Association of American Colleges & Universities and currently is a faculty fellow for the Science Education for New Civic Engagements and Responsibilities (SENCER) Project. She also has been a leader and speaker at the University of Wisconsin System's Women in Science Curriculum Reform Institute for the past five years. She did her undergraduate studies at Cornell University (1968-72), graduating Phi Beta Kappa, and earned her doctorate in Chemistry from the University of Wisconsin-Madison in 1976.

Caryn McTighe Musil

DR. CARYN MCTIGHE MUSIL is the vice-president of the office of diversity, equity, and global initiatives at the Association of American Colleges and Universities (AAC&U). She received her B.A. from Duke University and her M.A. and Ph.D. in English from Northwestern University. Dr. Musil is the project director for the three-year National Science Foundation grant, *Women and Scientific Literacy: Building Two-Way Streets.* From 1989-1991, she served as project director of a national, three-year research grant, "The Courage to Question: Women's Studies and Student Learning," awarded by the Fund for the Improvement of Postsecondary Education (FIPSE). Working with seven colleges and universities across the country to assess what students learn in women's studies courses. Dr. Musil edited three publications that emerged from the grant, the last of which was on assessment. She also was a co-author of *Liberal Learning and the Women's Studies Major.*

Marjorie Olmstead

DR. MARJORIE OLMSTEAD is a professor of physics and an adjunct professor of chemistry at the University of Washington, where she enjoys interacting with her students through both teaching and research. She began working at the University of Washington in 1991. Prior to that, she held a faculty position at the University of California, Berkeley and served as a member of the research staff at Xerox Palo Alto Research Center, where she developed her interest in exploring the basic physics underlying advances in micro- and nano-electronics. Prof. Olmstead and her students are researching atomic-scale processes by which interfaces form between dissimilar materials and properties of structures where at least one dimension is most easily measured in atoms. Prof. Olmstead has received several awards for her research, including the Peter Mark Memorial Award of the American Vacuum Society, the Maria Geoppert-Mayer Award of the American Physical Society and an Alexander von Humboldt Research Award. She served as chair of the American Physical Society Committee on the Status of Women in Physics in 1999-2000.

Joan Peckham

DR. JOAN PECKHAM is an associate professor of computer science and statistics at the University of Rhode Island. She earned her Ph.D. at University of Connecticut in 1990. Her areas of interest are database systems, semantic modeling, architectural design, active databases, and object-oriented design. She is interested in the issues of underrepresented groups in computing, and has been a leader in developing several programs and projects for enable computer-friendly access for undergraduate students.

Mercedes Rivero-Hudec

DR. MERCEDES RIVERO-HUDEC is an associate professor of chemical engineering at the University of Rhode Island. Her research program is in the area of transport phenomena at molecular and cellular level, with biomedical and environmental applications. Dr. Rivero is interested in the development of theoretical and in vitro models that closely represent actual conditions in vivo, and that allow for systematic and quantitative transport studies. Dr. Rivero was a visiting fellow in the chemical engineering section of the National Institutes of Health and a faculty member in the department of thermodynamics and transport phenomena at Universidad Simon Bolivar, Venezuela. As part of the *Women and Scientific Literacy* project she implemented several teaching techniques in undergraduate courses; co-led the engineering bridge camp for incoming first-year female engineering students; and was a participant in the SMET teaching fellows learning community.

Katrin Schultheiss

DR. KATRIN SCHULTHEISS is an assistant professor of history and of gender and women's studies at the University of Illinois at Chicago. She served as the Women's Studies representative on the UIC team participating in the AAC&U's "Building Two-Way Streets" initiative. She is the author of the book *Bodies and Souls: Politics and the Professionalization of Nursing in France, 1880-1922* (Harvard University Press: Cambridge, Mass, 2001). Her current research concerns the relationship between art and science in Europe at the turn of the twentieth century.

Karen Stein

DR. KAREN STEIN is a professor of English and women's studies, and director of graduate studies in English at the University of Rhode Island. She received her B.A. from Brooklyn College in 1962, M.A. from Pennsylvania State University in 1966, and Ph.D. from the University of Connecticut in 1982. She was one of the co-founders of the women's studies program at URI. She has written and spoken about women as writers and subjects of literature. Her current research interests include Nobel Laureate Toni Morrison, American women poets, utopian fiction by women, and women and science. She is writing a book on Canadian novelist, critic, and poet, Margaret Atwood. In 2000 she was a co-principal investigator on the NSF grant funded by the Course, Curriculum and Laboratory Improvement (CCLI) Program.

Banu Subramaniam

DR. BANU SUBRAMANIAM is an assistant research professor with the departments of women's studies and ecology and evolutionary biology at the University of Arizona. Her work seeks to engage feminism and sociology with the practice of science.

Maria V. Tahamont

DR. MARIA V. TAHAMONT is an associate professor of biological sciences and coordinator of Rowan seminar, the first year experience for students at Rowan University. She participated in and facilitated part of the faculty development research seminar on gender and science and was part of a three person team that devised and taught a new course entitled "Issues in Women's Health." For the New Jersey Project on Inclusive Education, she speaks on feminist pedagogy in the science classroom, scientific literacy, and diversity in the sciences. She recently coordinated the faculty workshop to develop interdisciplinary, team taught courses for first year students that address issues of diversity and democracy.

Thomas J. Wenzel

DR. THOMAS J. WENZEL is the Charles A. Dana professor of chemistry and a member of the environmental studies program at Bates College. He conducts research with undergraduates on the development of chiral nuclear magnetic resonance shift reagents, and teaches upper-level courses on analytical chemistry. His desire to increase the participation of underrepresented groups in chemistry led to his involvement in faculty development seminars at Bates on the connection between women's studies and the sciences. His participation in these seminars has had a significant impact on his teaching of general chemistry and led to his development of a new course "Women in Chemistry." He received the J. Calvin Giddings Award for Excellence in Education from the Analytical Division of the American Chemical Society in 1999, and he was recognized as the Maine Professor of the Year by the Carnegie Foundation in 1997. He also writes a regular column on educational topics for the journal *Analytical Chemistry*.

Appendices

Appendix A
Women and Scientific Literacy:
Building Two-Way Streets

Participating Institutions and Faculty

PARTICIPATING INSTITUTIONS

University of Arizona, *Tucson, AZ*
Barnard College, *New York, NY*
Bates College, *Lewiston, ME*
California State University, Long Beach, *Long Beach, CA*
Greenfield Community College, *Greenfield, MA*
University of Illinois at Chicago, *Chicago, IL*
Portland State University, *Portland, OR*
University of Rhode Island, *Kingston, RI*
Rowan University, *Glassboro, NJ*
Saint Lawrence University, *Canton, NY*

PARTICIPATING FACULTY

BARNARD COLLEGE

Laura Kay, *Team Leader, Physics/Astronomy*
Elizabeth Boylan, *Provost/Biology*
Lila Braine, *Psychology*
Sally Chapman, *Chemistry*
Lorrin Johnson, *Biology*
Ruth McChesney, *Biology*

Kelly Moore, *Sociology*
Afsaneh Najmabadi, *Women's Studies*
Teresa Rogers, *Sociology*
Susan Riemer Sacks, *Education*
Polly Wheat, *Medicine*

BATES COLLEGE

Bonnie J. Shulman, *Team Leader,*
  Mathematics
Pamela J. Baker, *Biology*
Sharon Kinsman, *Biology*

Georgia N. Nigro, *Psychology*
Mark D. Semon, *Physics*
Elizabeth H. Tobin, *History*

CALIFORNIA STATE UNIVERSITY, LONG BEACH

Laura Kingsford, *Team Leader, Biology*
Julie Bianchini, *Science Education*
Angela Bowen, *Women's Studies/English*
Barbara Bragonier, *Women's Studies*
Carol Itatani, *Biology*

Margaret Merryfield, *Chemistry/Biochemistry*
Patricia Rozee, *Women's Studies/Psychology*
Toni Stanton, *Biology/Anatomy-Physiology*
David Whitney, *Psychology*
Marcus Young Owl, *Anthropology*

GREENFIELD COMMUNITY COLLEGE

Ana Gaillat, *Team Leader, Chemistry*
Linda M. Cavanaugh, *Mathematics*
Beth Erviti, *Biology*
Melinda Gougeon, *Mathematics*

Peter Letson, *Physics*
Peter Rosnick, *Mathematics*
Anne Wiley, *Psychology*

PORTLAND STATE UNIVERSITY

Johanna Brenner, *Co-Team Leader,*
  Women's Studies/Sociology
Linda George, *Co-Team Leader, Chemistry*
Lois Becker, *History*

Michael Flower, *Biology*
Monica Halka, *Physics*
Jack Straton, *Physics*

ROWAN UNIVERSITY

Virginia Brown, *Team Leader, Psychology*
Janet Caldwell, *Mathematics*
Janet Lindman, *History/Women's Studies*

Karen Magee-Sauer, *Physics*
Maria V. Tahamont, *Biology*
Hieu Nguyen, *Mathematics*

ST. LAWRENCE UNIVERSITY

Catherine Jahncke, *Co-Team Leader, Physics*
Valerie Lehr, *Co-Team Leader,*
  Government/Gender Studies
Maegan Bos, *Mathematics*
Carol Budd, *Biology*

Judith DeGroat, *History*
David Hornung, *Biology*
Karen Johnson, *Physics*
Joan Larsen, *Research Librarian*
Nadia Marano, *Chemistry*

UNIVERSITY OF ARIZONA

Laura Briggs, *Co-Team Leader, Women's Studies*

Marta Civil, *Mathematics*

Susan Craddock, *Women's Studies/Geography*

Jennifer Croissant, *Material Science and Engineering*

Sharla Fett, *History*

Jennifer Franklin, *Instructional Assessment*

Mary Poulton, *Mining and Geologic Engineering*

Banu Subramaniam, *Co-Team Leader, Women's Studies/Ecology/ Evolutionary Biology*

Connie Walker, *Astronomy*

Martha Whittaker, *Hydrology/Women's Studies*

UNIVERSITY OF ILLINOIS AT CHICAGO

Alice Dan, *Team Leader, Nursing*

Sharon M. Fetzer, *Chemistry*

Rebecca Gordon, *Women's Affairs*

Sheila McNicholas, *Mathematics*

Arlene Norsym, *Engineering*

Suzanne Poirier, *Medical Education*

Brenda Russell, *Physiology/Bio-Physics*

Katrin Schultheiss, *Women's Studies/History*

Stacy A. Wenzel, *Center for Research on Women and Gender*

Donald Wink, *Chemistry*

UNIVERSITY OF RHODE ISLAND

Donna M. Hughes, *Team leader, Women's Studies*

G. Faye Boudreaux-Bartels, *Electrical Engineering*

Nancy Eaton, *Mathematics*

Marian Goldsmith, *Biological Sciences*

Lisa Harlow, *Psychology*

Linda Hufnagel, *Biochemistry/Microbiology*

Doris Kirchner, *Languages*

Lenore Martin, *Pharmacy*

Joan Peckham, *Computer Sciences/Statistics*

Mary Ellen Reilly, *Women's Studies/Sociology*

Mercedes A. Rivero-Hudec, *Chemical Engineering*

Karen Stein, *English/Women's Studies*

Betty J. Young, *Education*

Appendix B
Women and Scientific Literacy: Building Two-Way Streets

Advisory Board

Margaret Palmer
Professor of Biology, University of Maryland

Karen Barad
Chair of Women's Studies, Professor of Women's Studies and Philosophy, Mount Holyoke College

Angela B. Ginorio
Associate Professor of Women Studies, University of Washington

Evelynn Hammonds
Associate Professor of the History of Science, Program in Science, Technology & Society,
Massachusetts Institute of Technology

Cathy Middlecamp
Director, Chemistry Learning Center, University of Wisconsin–Madison

Bonnie Spanier
Associate Professor of Women's Studies, University at Albany–SUNY

Joan Poliner Shapiro
Assessment Consultant, Professor of Educational Leadership and Policy Studies,
Temple University

Appendix C
Women and Scientific Literacy: Building Two-Way Streets Sample Syllabi

The Women and Scientific Literacy project continues AAC&U's strong tradition of fostering systemic curricular change that improves the quality and scope of student learning. The primary goal of this project is to bridge the gulf between science and women's studies by incorporating the new scholarship in these areas into undergraduate science, engineering, and mathematics courses and also by making science a more central part of women's studies courses.

This appendix includes syllabi from the courses described in the articles above. Other sample syllabi developed as part of this project can be found on the AAC&U's web site at www.aacu-edu.org/womenscilit.

THE UNIVERSITY OF ILLINOIS AT CHICAGO
WOMEN'S HEALTH ISSUES

INSTRUCTOR:
Katrin Schultheiss
kschulth@uic.edu

FALL 1999

COURSE DESCRIPTION:
This interdisciplinary seminar explores the history, politics, and ethics of women's health
concerns. Through a combination of assigned reading, class discussion, oral presentations, and independent research, students will explore such topics as the meaning of
childbirth in the past and present, the racial politics of reproductive rights, feminist analyses of women and depression, and the ongoing efforts to build a women's health movement.

READINGS:
Natalie Angier, *Woman: An Intimate Geography*
Anne Fausto-Sterling, *Myths of Gender*
Fine and Asch, eds. *Women with Disabilities*
Dana Crowley Jack, *Silencing the Self: Women and Depression*
Sharlene Hesse-Biber, *Am I Thin Enough Yet? The Cult of Thinness and the
    Commercialization of Identity*
Judith Walker Leavitt, *Brought to Bed*
Kristen Luker, *Abortion and the Politics of Motherhood*
Emily Martin, *The Woman in the Body*
Elaine Tyler May, *Barren in the Promised Land*
Dorothy Roberts, *Killing the Black Body*
Karen Stabiner, *To Dance with the Devil: The New War on Breast Cancer*

WEEK 1: INTRODUCTION
Discussion: What is Health?

WEEK 2: THEMES
*Ruzek, Olesen, Clarke, "Social, Biomedical, and Feminist Models of Women's Health"
*— "What are the Dynamics of Difference"
*Wingard, "Patterns and Puzzles"
all in Ruzek, Olesen, Clark, *Women's Health: Complexities and Differences*

*Edward H. Beardsley, "Race as a Factor in Health," in Apple, ed., *Women, Health and Medicine in America*

WEEK 3: WOMEN'S BIOLOGY
*Angier, *Woman: An Intimate Geography*

WEEK 4: POLITICS OF SEXUAL DIFFERENCE
Fausto-Sterling, *Myths of Gender*, chaps. 1-3, 6,7.

WEEK 5: HISTORY OF CHILDBEARING
Leavitt, *Brought to Bed*, 3-141
Roberts, *Killing the Black Body*, 3-55

WEEK 6: CONTEMPORARY ISSUES IN CHILDBEARING
Leavitt, finish
Martin, ch. 4,5,8,9

WEEK 7: MOTHERHOOD AND FEMALE IDENTITY
May, *Barren in the Promised Land: Childless Americans and the Pursuit of Happiness*

WEEK 8: "WOMEN'S PATHOLOGIES": MENSTRUATION, MENOPAUSE
Martin, 3,6
Fausto-Sterling, *Myths of Gender*, chap. 4,5
MIDTERM EXAMS DUE IN CLASS

WEEK 9: RACE AND REPRODUCTIVE RIGHTS
Roberts, *Killing the Black Body*, 104-312 (skim chap. 2)

WEEK 10: THE ABORTION DEBATE
Luker, *Abortion and the Politics of Motherhood*
*Faludi, *Backlash*, chap.14

WEEK 11: MENTAL ILLNESS
*Tomes, "Historical Perspectives on Women and Mental Illness" in Apple, *Women, Health, and Medicine in America*
Jack, *Silencing the Self: Women and Depression* (NY, 1993)

WEEK 12: BODY IMAGE
Hesse-Biber, *Am I Thin Enough Yet? The Cult of Thinness and the Commercialization of Identity (NY, 1997)*
PAPER DUE IN CLASS

WEEK 13: WOMEN AND DISABILITY

*Gill, "The Last Sisters: Health Issues of Women with Disabilities" in *Women's Health: Complexities and Differences*

Fine and Asch, *Women with Disabilities: Essays in Psychology, Culture and Politics,* (Temple, 1988), selections

WEEK 14: WOMEN'S HEALTH ACTIVISM: TOWARD A WOMEN'S HEALTH MOVEMENT

Stabiner, *To Dance with the Devil: The New War on Breast Cancer* (NY, 1998)

WEEK 15: CLASS PROJECTS, DISCUSSION

THE UNIVERSITY OF ILLINOIS AT CHICAGO

WOMEN'S BODIES, WOMEN'S LIVES: A SOCIAL HISTORY OF MEDICINE

INSTRUCTOR:
Katrin Schultheiss
kschulth@uic.edu

FALL 1999

COURSE DESCRIPTION:
This seminar explores the history and politics of women's health primarily in the United States by focussing on three broad and interrelated questions: How has the physical functioning of the female body been interpreted by the scientific community? How have scientific and broader cultural interpretations of the sexualized female body shaped the type and quality of medical care offered to women? What have women done to change ideas about women's bodies and health and the medical care offered to women? We will devote a considerable amount of time to the social and cultural history of women's reproductive functions including menstruation, pregnancy, childbirth, and menopause as well as the development of obstetrics and midwifery. We will also explore such topics as women's entry into the male-dominated medical profession, the changing diagnosis and experience of anorexia nervosa, the cultural meanings of madness, and the politics of women's healthcare today.

READINGS:
Janet Ferris Brodie, *Contraception and Abortion in Nineteenth Century America*
Joan Brumberg, *Fasting Girls: The History of Anorexia Nervosa* (1988)
Hine, Darlene Clark, *Black Women in White*
Hubbard, Ruth, *The Politics of Women's Biology*
Leavitt, *Brought to Bed: Childbearing in America, 1750-1950* (1986)
Morantz-Sanchez, Regina, *Sympathy and Science*
* indicates reading is part of photocopied packet available from instructor

WEEK 1: INTRODUCTION
Discussion: What is a feminist history of medicine? Is gender relevant to understanding science? Is science/medicine sexist?

WEEK 2: THEORETICAL FRAMEWORK: GENDERING SCIENCE/GENDERING THE BODY
Reading:　　Hubbard, chaps. 2,3,7-10 (22-42, 87-140)
　　　　　　　* Schiebinger, selections from *The Mind Has No Sex?* and *Nature's Body*
　　　　　　　* Fausto-Sterling, *Myths of Gender*, ch. 7, 205-222

WEEK 3: REPRODUCTION AND CHILDBIRTH IN AMERICA: A HISTORY
Reading: Leavitt, intro., chaps. 1-5 (3-141)

WEEK 4: REPRODUCTION AND CHILDBIRTH: CULTURAL ANALYSIS
Reading: Leavitt, finish
              *Martin, chaps. 1,2,8,9,11

WEEK 5: THE CONTROL OF REPRODUCTION
Reading: Contraception and Abortion, selections.
PAPER #1 DUE

WEEK 6: MENSTRUATION AND MENOPAUSE
Reading: *Martin, chaps. 3,5,6,10
              * Bullough and Voght, "Women, Menstruation, and Nineteenth-Century
                Medicine," *Bulletin of the History of Medicine* 47 (1973): 66-82.
              *Fausto-Sterling, ch. 4, 90-122
              **The Curse,* selections

WEEK 7: TREATING "WOMEN'S DISEASES"
              *Ehrenreich and English, *For Her Own Good,* chap. 4 "The Sexual Politics of Sickness"
              Morantz-Sanchez, ch. 8.
Discussion of final projects

WEEK 8: GENDER AND MADNESS
Reading: *Showalter, *The Female Malady,* chs. 5, 6.
              *Theriot, "Women's Voices in Nineteenth Century Medical Discourse," *Signs*
                19 (Autumn 1993): 1-25.
\WEEK 9: DISEASE AS CULTURAL SYMBOL: HISTORY OF ANOREXIA NERVOSA
Reading: Brumberg, chaps. 1- 6

WEEK 10: POLITICS OF BODY SIZE
Reading: Brumberg, finish
              *Bordo, "Anorexia Nervosa," "Reading the Slender Body" in *Unbearable
                Weight: Feminism, Western Culture, and the Body.*
              *Haiken, *Venus Envy,* selections
PAPER #2 DUE

WEEK 11: WOMEN AS HEALTH CARE PRACTITIONERS: NURSES
Reading: Hine, *Black Women in White*

WEEK 12: WOMEN ENTER THE MEDICAL PROFESSION I
Reading: Morantz-Sanchez, ch. 3-7 (47-202)

WEEK 13: WOMEN ENTER THE MEDICAL PROFESSION II
Reading: Morantz-Sanchez, ch.9-12 (232-361)

WEEK 14: WOMEN, CULTURE, AND "ALTERNATIVE" HEALING
Reading: Choose from list of books distributed in class

WEEK 15: CONCLUSIONS. PRESENTATIONS OF FINAL RESEARCH PROJECTS.

ROWAN UNIVERSITY

ISSUES IN WOMEN'S HEALTH

INSTRUCTORS:
Virginia Brown
brown@rowan.edu

Janet Moore Lindman
lindman@rowan.edu

Maria Tahamont
tahamont@rowan.edu

SPRING 2000

COURSE DESCRIPTION:
This interdisciplinary course critically examines issues in women's health. Biological, sociocultural, psychological, historical, and political processes that shape and define women's health and healthcare experiences will be explored, including ways in which medical knowledge has been constructed and applied to women's bodies. It is a primary goal to explore these significant questions: How has the physical functioning of the human female body been interpreted by the scientific community? How have these interpretations shaped the type and quality of medical treatment available to women? What has been done to change ideas about women's bodies and the health care offered to women? What are the links between cultural perceptions of women, women's status, and the management of women's bodies?

THE OBJECTIVES OF THE COURSE:
- to examine the physiology underlying women's health and illness experiences
- to examine the methodology used by scientific research in the study of women's health
- to examine women's health issues in their social, cultural, and historical contexts
- to expose hidden issues in women's health, for example

GOALS FOR THE STUDENTS:
Upon completion of the course the students will be able:
- to interpret statistical data related to women's health issues
- to examine data using contextual analysis
- to demonstrate an understanding of the social, cultural, and historical factors that affect the ways that women's bodies are conceptualized and women's health issues are viewed
- to assess the strengths and limitations of research in the field of women's health

- to critically analyze policy issues and decisions made about women's health and healthcare
- to understand the link between gender relations and women's status in contemporary society and medical treatment and research

STUDENT RESPONSIBILITIES:
- Group Project - oral presentation and written self-assessment
- Journal (to be handed in twice during semester)
- Reaction Papers (3-4 pages, 3 per semester)
- Class Participation, small group work, and email discussions

GROUP PRESENTATIONS:
Possible Topics: teenage pregnancy; sexually transmitted diseases; breast cancer; cardiovascular disease and treatment; alcoholism; exercise; abortion; Lamaze and natural childbirth; women with disabilities; cosmetic surgery; female genital mutilation; environmental racism.

COURSE TOPICS AND READINGS:
WEEK 1: INTRODUCTION
Who are we as a class? What do the students want out of this class? What are the goals and interests of the students? Body image exercise

WEEK 2: THE BIG PICTURE
How is Gender Relevant to Science? Is Medicine/Science Sexist? What is the Impact of a Person's Gender, Race, Ethnicity, Class and Sexual Orientation on the Quality of the Health Care They Receive?

Readings: Lisa Collier Cool, *Forgotten Women: How Minorities are Under Served by our Health Care System.*
Diane Hales, *What Doctors Don't Know About Women's Bodies.*
Emily Martin, *The Egg and the Sperm: How Science Has Constructed a Romance Based on Stereotypical Male-Female Roles.*
Christine Northrop, *Physician, Heal Thyself.*
Jocelyn White and Wendy Levinson, *Primary Care of Lesbian Patients.*

WEEK 3: BODY IMAGE I
Fat as a Feminist Issue. Thinness as Chic. Media Images of the Female Body

Readings: Susan Bordo, *The Body and the Reproduction of Femininity.*
Susan Bordo, *Reading the Slender Body.*
Susie Orbach, *Fat is a Feminist Issue.*
Christine Smith, *Women, Weight and Body Image.*
FILM: *Slim Hopes: Advertising and the Obsession with Thinness*

WEEK 4: BODY IMAGE II

Metabolism: the Story behind Fat. The Culture of Diet. The History of Obesity and Anorexia

Readings: Sara Hare, *You're Not Fat, You're Living in the Wrong Country.*

Marini, Bartholomew, and Welch, *Nutrition and Metabolism.*

Christine Northrop, *Nourishing Ourselves with Food.*

Kathleen Pike and Ruth Striegel-Moore, *Disordered Eating and Eating Disorders.*

First Reaction Paper Due

WEEK 5: FEMALE HORMONES AND THE MYTH OF PMS

Menstrual Cycle/Ovarian Cycle. Why Do Only American Women Experience PMS?
Medicalizing Natural Body Changes into "Symptoms," The Culture of Menopause

Readings: Natalie Angier, *Suckers and Horns: The Prodigal Uterus.*

Joan Jacobs Brumberg, *The Body's New Timetable: How the Life Course of American Girls Has Changed.*

Carol Tavris, *Misdiagnosing the Body: Pre-Menstrual Syndrome, Post-Menstrual Syndrome, and Other 'Normal' Diseases.*

Emily Martin, *Medical Metaphors of Women's Bodies: Menstruation and Menopause.*

WEEK 6: SOCIAL POLITICS I

Midwives and Women Healers. Scientific Motherhood. Childbirth and Science.

Readings: Rima Apple, *Constructing Mothers: Scientific Motherhood in the Nineteenth and Twentieth Centuries.*

Judith Walzer Leavitt, *Birthing and Anesthesia: The Debate Over Twilight Sleep.*

Emily Martin, *Medical Metaphors of Women's Bodies: Birth.*

Laurel Thatcher Ulrich, *'The Living Mother of a Living Child': Midwifery and Mortality in Post-Revolutionary New England.*

FILM: *A Midwife's Tale*

WEEK 7: SOCIAL POLITICS II

Birth Control and Abortion. Reproductive Rights. Women and Welfare.

Readings: Harry Blackmun, segment of "Roe v. Wade, 1973."

Linda Gordon, *Voluntary Motherhood: The Beginnings of Feminist Birth Control Ideas in the United States.*

Loretta Ross, *African American Women and Abortion, 1800-1970.*

About Welfare: Myths, Facts, Challenges, and Solutions.

Second Reaction Paper Due

Journals Due

WEEK 8: SEXUAL HEALTH AND SEXUAL DISEASE
  AIDS. Racism, Sexism, Classism, Heterosexism in AIDS. International Issues and AIDS.
Readings: Kathryn Anastos and Carola Marte, *Women—The Missing Persons in the AIDS Epidemic*.
          Paula Treichler, *AIDS, Gender, and Biomedical Discourses: Current Contests for Meaning*.
          African-American Women Respond to AIDS/HIV.
          Addressing Africa's Agony, Time article.
          Many Women at Risk for HIV Still not Using Condoms.
FILM: *AIDS: The Women Speak*

WEEK 9: BIOLOGICAL AND SOCIAL CONSTRUCTIONS OF MENTAL HEALTH
  Depression: Biological or Cultural? Impact of Gender, Race, Class and Culture on
  Mental Health Care.
Readings: Ellen Abelson, *The Invention of Kleptomania*.
          Ellen Leibenluft, *Why Are So Many Women Depressed?*
          Carol Tavris, *Misdiagnosing the Mind: Why Women are Sick, and Men Have Problems*.
Third Reaction Paper Due

WEEK 10: GENDERING OF ADDICTIONS
  Physiology of Addiction. Usage and Treatment. Cultural Images of Female vs. Male
  Addicts
Readings: Cornell University National Center on Addiction and *Substance Abuse*,
          Substance Abuse and the American Woman, (packet of readings).
          Pamela Jumper-Thurman and Barbara Plested, *Health Needs of American-Indian Women*.
          Nancy P. Vogeltanz and Sharon C. Wilsnack, *Alcohol Problems in Women: Risk Factors, Consequences, and Treatment Strategies*.

WEEK 11: PROJECT PRESENTATIONS

WEEK 12: PROJECT PRESENTATIONS

WEEK 13: FINAL COMMENTS

WEEK 14: FINAL EXPERIENCE
Journals Due

UNIVERSITY OF WASHINGTON

ISSUES FOR ETHNIC MINORITIES AND WOMEN IN SCIENCE AND ENGINEERING

INSTRUCTORS:
Angela B. Ginorio
ginorio@u.washington.edu

Marjorie A. Olmstead
olmstead@phys.washington.edu

SPRING 1999

The goals for this class through all class activities are to:
- inform students of issues faced by women and ethnic minorities in science and engineering
- introduce students to expert women and ethnic minority practitioners of science as well as expert social scientists who study issues faced by women and ethnic minorities in science and engineering
- provide a national as well as local context for these issues so that students can critically evaluate the framing of the issues as well as the effectiveness of the solutions proposed so far
- prepare students to address these issues in the context of their own discipline and institution by developing review of possible solutions at the University of Washington.

SCHEDULE:
A. Overview of Status of Women and Ethnic Minorites in Science and Engineering
    1. Explain class goals and mechanics. Glossary of terms. Web tutorial.
    2. "Status of women in science and engineering, " Mary Frank Fox
       Introduced by *Dean, College of Arts and Sciences.*
    3. "Status of ethnic minorities in science," Shirley Malcom
       Introduced by *Vice President, Student Affairs.*
    4. Discussion on readings. Sorting and separating facts, statistics, anecdotes.
    5. "History of women at the University of Washington and ethnic minorities in science and engineering," Helen Remick, *Assistant Provost for Equal Opportunity*
    6. "Changes in our Lifetime," Ingrith Deyrup-Olsen, *emerita* and Gene Cota-Robles, *Latino biologist.*

B. Climate Issues and Successful Interventions
    1. "Classroom interventions," Patricia McGowan, *Director of the state-wide Mathematics, Engineering, and Science Achievement (MESA) program,* and Paula Heron, *Assistant Professor in the Physics Education Group*

2. "Non-curricular interventions," Suzanne Brainard, then *Director of the Women in Science and Engineering WISE) Program and founding member of the Women in Engineering Programs Advocates Network (WEPAN),* Patrick Stayton, *Associate Professor and Advisor to the University of Washington's Society for the Advancement of Chicanos and Native Americans in Science (SACNAS) chapter.*
   "Status of underrepresented minorities at medical school," *student presentation.*
3. "Climate at the student level," *student presentation*
   "Climate at the professional level," *student presentation.*
4. "Mentoring," *student presentation*
   "Stereotypes and access," *student presentation.*
5. "Lives and contributions of minority and women scientists," *student presentation.*
   Discussion on university and industry programs to improve status.
6. "Teaching styles, learning styles: The case from engineering," Karan Watson
   Introduced by *Dean, Graduate School.*
7. "The Heroic Engineer," Taft Broome
   Introduced by *Dean, College of Engineering.*

C. Policy Review and Agenda for Action
   1. "Human resources for science, technology, and the nation: National policies, local actions," Darryl Chubin, Introduced by *University President*
   2. "Affirmative action," *student presentation.*
      "Maternity leave policies," *student presentation.*
   3. Discussion of the MIT Report
   4. Discussion of policy memo goals and structure.
   5. "Progress for Women: Lessons from California and Elsewhere." Laurel Wilkening
      Introduced by *Regent.*
   6. Finalize agenda for action.

Assignments:
1. Report a statistic related to this class with a comparison of at least five instances. Write an explanation of what the number indicates and what is its significance with regard to the topics of this class. (1-2 pages)
2. Report on a specific individual who made a unique or historically significant contribution to issues related to this course. Document your claim of their uniqueness or historical significance. (1-2 pages)
3. Write a personal reflection on how a reading or speaker for the climate issues portion of the class impacted your thinking or experience. (3 pages)
4. For your assigned department at the University of Washington, find out the name, year of Ph.D., year of hire, and year left University (if no longer here) of the first minority male/female and first white male/female who was a) tenured or tenure-track faculty member, b) chair, c) graduate with BS/BA, MS/MA, and Ph.D. For the most recent year available, determine the ethnic and gender breakdown of graduates and faculty at each level (BS/BA, MS/MA, Ph.D., Asst. Prof., Assoc. Prof., Full Prof., Chair).

5. Write a policy memo addressing an issue related to this class. Choose an issue and write an argument for what could be done that would make a positive difference for ethnic minorities and women in science and engineering. You should address your memo to a particular person or officer, who has the power to implement your proposal. (1-3 pages)

6. Make a presentation in class, either individually or as a group, on a topic of interest to the class. (20 minutes/person) You need to provide an abstract, reading material for the class, and a list of references to be posted on the class web page several days prior to your presentation. A three-page report on your presentation (submitted individually) is due one week after the presentation.

7. Evaluate each student presentation (except your own) using the web-based form. This will count both as part of your class participation grade and as part of the evaluated student's presentation grade.

8. Write a summary of one panel or guest speaker presentation in a format suitable for posting on the course web page (less than 600 words). Sign up in pairs during the first week of class.

9. For those students taking the course for 5 credits, an additional project is required. You should choose one specific issue related to this class and explore it in depth. Your report should include a clear thesis or purpose, fulfill this purpose, and detail conclusions that may be deduced from the materials presented. It should be accurate, creative, and well-referenced. A written proposal must be submitted one month before the due date, and must be approved by one of the instructors.

LECTURES:
The Status of Women in Science, Engineering and Mathematics
MARY FRANK FOX, Professor of Women, Science and Technology,
    Georgia Institute of Technology
Introduced by DAVID HODGE, Dean of College of Arts and Sciences

Status of Ethnic Minorities in Science, Engineering and Mathematics
SHIRLEY MALCOM, Director, Education and Human Resources Programs, American
    Association for the Advancement of Science, UW 1998 Alumna of the Year
Introduced by ERNEST MORRIS, Vice-President for Student Affairs

Teaching Styles and Learning Styles: The Case for Engineering
KARAN WATSON, Professor of Electrical Engineering and Associate Dean of Graduate and
    Undergraduate Studies, Texas A&M University
Introduced by MARSHA LANDOLT, Dean, UW Graduate School

The Heroic Engineer
TAFT BROOME, Professor of Civil Engineering , Howard University
Introduced by DENISE DENTON, Dean, UW College of Engineering

Human Resources for Science, Technology, and t-he Nation: National Policies, Local Actions
DARYL CHUBIN, Senior Policy Associate, National Science Board Office, Division
    Director for Research, Evaluation, and Communication, National Science Foundation,
    Adjunct Professor of Science and Technology Studies, Virginia Tech
Introduced by RICHARD MCCORMICK, President, University of Washington

Progress for Women: Lessons from California and Elsewhere
LAUREL WILKENING, Former Chancellor, University of California, Irvine, Former
    Provost, University of Washington
Introduced by MARI CLACK, Regent, University of Washington

UNIVERSITY OF RHODE ISLAND

INTERNATIONAL WOMEN'S ISSUES

http://www.uri.edu/artsci/wms/hughes/interw99.htm

INSTRUCTOR:
Donna M. Hughes
dhughes@uri.edu

FALL 1999

COURSE DESCRIPTION:
This course covers issues on women/gender and colonialism and neo-colonialism, nationalism, liberation struggles, democratization, development, environmental degradation, human rights, and women's movements and activism. Topics will be examined using women's autobiographies and essays and films.

REQUIRED READINGS:
Global Gender Issues-Dilemmas in World Politics, Second Edition, V. Spike Peterson and
    Anne Sisson Runyan, Westview Press, 1999.
Nawal El Saadawi Reader, Nawal El Saadawi, Zed Books, 1997.
*When Heaven and Earth Changed Places-A Vietnamese Woman's Journey from War to
    Peace,* Le Ly Hayslip with Jay Wurts, Doubleday, 1989.
Daughters of the Pacific, Zohl de Ishtar, Spinifex Press, 1994.
*Comfort Woman-A Filipina's Story of Prostitution and Slavery Under the Japanese
    Military,* Maria Rosa Henson, Rowan & Littlefield, 1999.

CLASS PROCEDURES:
   For *class discussions,* you are expected to make a conscientious commitment to come to class, be prepared for, and take part in the discussions. At the beginning of each class, I will ask each person to suggest topics for that day's discussion.
   Reading Response Journal. Keep a journal/notebook in which you record the main points from your reading (a brief outline and summary of main points). Make connections between readings. Note commonalties and differences in women's experiences from different regions in the world. Record your thoughts and reactions to the readings.
   Research Papers: Research and write a paper on a topic related to international women's issues. Papers should include your analysis of material and situations. Research papers should be approximately 12 pages (3000 words) in length. Each paper should include an historical context for a contemporary topic and at least 10 references/sources for information in the paper.

COURSE OUTLINE AND READING ASSIGNMENTS:
Week 1: Introduction. Film: *Femmes aux yeux ouverts (Women with open eyes)*.

Week 2: Theoretical Overview.
    Readings: Chap 1. The Gender of World Politics, *Global Gender Issues*
    Chap 2. Gender as a Lens on World Politics, *Global Gender Issues*

Week 3: Women's Lives and Revolution. Film: *In the Year of the Pig*
    Readings: "Women and Revolution in Vietnam," Mary Ann Tétreault (handout)
    Prologue, Chap 1-7, *When Heaven and Earth Changed Places*, Le Ly Hayslip

Week 4: Women's Lives and Revolution. Film: *Heaven and Earth*.
    Readings: Chap 8-14, Epilogue, *When Heaven and Earth Changed Places*, Le Ly Hayslip
    "Only Women: Maternal Soldiers," "Picking Up the Pieces: Going Home," and "A
        Rice Meal Without Rice: The Costs of War," *Even the Women Must Fight -
        Memories of War from North Vietnam*, Karen Gottschang.

Week 5: Gender and Power. Due: Reading Journal #1.
    Readings: Chap 3 Gendered Divisions of Power, *Global Gender Issues*.
    Introduction, *Nawal El Saadawi Reader*.
    Chap 1. Women and the Poor: The Challenge of global justice,
        Nawal El Saadawi Reader.
    Chap 2. Women in the South in Relation to Women in the North,
        Nawal El Saadawi Reader.
    The Pacific Is Our Home, *Daughters of the Pacific*.

Week 6: Militarism and Security. Film: *Savage Acts: Wars, Fairs and Empires*.
    Readings: Chap 4 pp. 113-147, Gendered Divisions of Violence, Labor and
        Resources, *Global Gender Issues*.
    *Comfort Woman-A Filipina's Story of Prostitution and Slavery Under the Japanese
        Military*, Maria Rosa Henson.

Week 7: Culture.
    Readings: Chap 12. Why Keep Asking Me About My Identity, *Nawal El Saadawi Reader*.
    Chap 13. Women, Religion and Literature: Bridging the Cultural Gap, *Nawal El
        Saadawi Reader*.

Week 8: Environment and Ecology.
    Readings: Chap 4 pp. 147-156, *Gendered Divisions of Violence, Labor and Resources,
        Global Gender Issues*.
    Fire in the Water-The Marshall Islands, *Daughters of the Pacific*.
    Behind a Curtain of Flowers-Tahiti-Polynesia, *Daughters of the Pacific*.
    Tourism Is Not Good for Children-The Northern Marianas, *Daughters of the Pacific*.

Week 9: Women's Health. Film: *Rites*. Due: Reading Journal #2.
  Readings: Chap 6. Women and Health in the Arab World, *Nawal El Saadawi Reader*.
  Chap 7. The Bitter Lot of Women, *Nawal El Saadawi Reader*.

Week 10: Fundamentalism. Film: *The Situation of Women in Iran*.
  Readings: Chap 9. Islamic Fundamentalism and Women, Nawal El Saadawi Reader.
  Chap 10. The Impact of Fanatic Religious Thought: A Story of a young Egyptian
    Muslim woman, *Nawal El Saadawi Reader*.
  Chap 11. Fundamentalism: Old Friend, New Enemy, *Nawal El Saadawi Reader*.

Week 11: Slavery and Exploitation. Film: *Bought and Sold*.
  Readings: "The New Slavery," *Disposable People: New Slavery in the Global Economy*.
  Kevin Bales, "Thailand: Because She Looks Like a Child," *Disposable People: New
    Slavery in the Global Economy*, Kevin Bales.

Week 12: Women and Resistance. Film: *Women-Voice of the Oppressed*. Due: Research Paper.
  Readings: Chap 5. The Politics of Resistance: Women as Nonstate, Antistate and
    Transstate Actors, *Global Gender Issues*.
  Chap 15. Dissidence and Creativity, *Nawal El Saadawi Reader*.
  Chap 22. Women in Resistance: The Arab World, *Nawal El Saadawi Reader*.
  The Spirit of Resistance, *Daughters of the Pacific*.

Week 13: International Women's Issues Symposium. Due: Reading Journal #3

UNIVERSITY OF RHODE ISLAND

WOMEN AND THE NATURAL SCIENCES

INSTRUCTOR:
Karen Stein
Karen_S@uri.edu

FALL 2000

COURSE DESCRIPTION:
Our investigation of women and science will take three main paths.

How has science studied women? Science has studied women as aberrations, as anomalies, and as deviations from a male norm. Thus, we often know a great deal more about men's health issues and treatments than about women's health issues. Now we are learning more about women's lives and bodies, because women are demanding representation. By the end of the course, you will be able to discuss some of the key scientific studies on women such as sociobiology, eugenics, and studies of women's hormones, IQ and health.

Who are the women scientists? By the end of the course, you will recognize the names and contributions of many women scientists.

How is science socially constructed? Women are beginning to ask questions about science and its methods. Science claims to be objective, but is that really the case? For example, how does the language of science determine what problems scientists study and how scientific work is funded? What influence do political issues have? Would science be different if more women enter the scientific fields? The example we will use in this course is the HGP, the Human Genome Project. By the end of the course, you will know what the HGP is and some of the ethical and legal questions it raises.

REQUIRED READINGS:
Our Babies, Ourselves: How Biology and Culture Shape the Way We Parent by Meredith F. Small
Rachel Carson: The Writer at Work by Paul Brooks
Walking With the Great Apes: Jane Goodall, Dian Fossey, Birute Galdikas by Sy Montgomery
Thinking Critically about Research on Sex and Gender by Caplan and Caplan
Renaissance Women of Science by Louise Van Der Does and Rita J. Simon
The Human Genome Project: Cracking the Code Within Us by Elizabeth L. Marshall
Recommended but not required: *Gender and Scientific Authority*

OTHER READINGS:
Kass-Simon and Farnes, *Women of Science: Righting the Record*
Margaret Rossiter, *Women Scientists*
Bordo, "Reading the Slender Body"
Small, "Aping Culture"

THE OBSERVATIONAL STUDY: Choose a wild animal to watch for 1/2 hour on each of three days. It could be a squirrel, a bird, an insect, etc. Keep a record of your observations. We will discuss the items to record, and what to watch for. Include date/time/weather/location of each observation. Include animal movement, reaction to you (if any), any other details.

MAGAZINE ANALYSIS. With your group, choose a magazine to review. Find images of men and women. Divide up the topics: ads, articles, fiction, other. Include 2-4 page report and sample ads. Count ads, articles, describe other features. What products do the ads present? Analyze the images of men and women in the ads and the articles. (What are they wearing? What are they doing? What kinds of people do they seem to be: jobs, ages, social status, appearance?) What is the magazine's circulation? Who reads it? What messages does it convey about men and women?

SCRAPBOOK. Keep a scrapbook of recent articles in newspapers and magazines about women and science. Must have at least 4 articles. Three may come from the internet. For each article, list date, source, title, author (if known). Summarize the main points of each article in 1-5 sentences. Write your comments about each article in 5-10 sentences.

ANNOTATED BIBLIOGRAPHY. Compile an annotated bibliography of books and articles related to your final project. Must include at least 6 sources. Author, title, date, place of publication, 1-5 sentence summary of each source, your discussion of the article or book. What do you find are its strong points, its weaknesses? How useful is it for your project? (5-15 sentences)

FINAL PROJECT. This may be done in a group of up to 3 students. It will include:
• submit your bibliography again;
• report of 3-7 pages. The report will include: statement of the problem or question you investigated. What you learned about the problem or question. Implications for women and/or science;
• the draft you showed the peer mentor with the comments;
• a non-print component related to your project. This could be a chart, a picture, a power point presentation, a video or audio tape, a skit, a game, a quiz for the class.

SCHEDULE:
I. Images of women scientists in popular films: what are the images? What stereotypes of men and women do these movies present? What messages do they convey? What beliefs about men and women do we hold?
   Week 1: Introduction to course. Video of women scientists in American popular films.

II. Women primatologists: the women in this field revolutionized the study of primates. How did they do so?

Week 2: Jane Goodall in Montgomery. Video *Among the Wild Chimpanzees.* Part I..
  Jane Goodall part II. Plan of the magazine analysis
Week 3: Dian Fossey in Montgomery. Video *Search for the Great Apes.*
  Do apes have language? Do they have culture? Small, *Aping Culture,* Sue Savage-
  Rumbaugh Field notes due.
Week 4: Birute Galdikas in Montgomery. *Video Search for the Great Apes.*

III. Images of women's bodies. What images do newspapers, print advertisements, and
  magazines convey? What impact do these images have?
  Week 5: Barbie presentation by Lisa Carter.
    Killing us softly III video. Lisa will do her magazine analysis.
  Week 6: "The Slender Body" by Susan Bordo (article on reserve in library) Plan of the bib-
    liography assignment. Presentation of magazine analysis. Present topics for final project.

IV. *Human Genome Project* Elizabeth Marshall
  What is the HGP? What prospects does it hold for changing the way we live? What are
  some of the issues and concerns? Is it more helpful or harmful to know the human
  genome sequence?
    Week 7: pp.7-50, 99-104 (Scene 1 and 2); pp. 51-98; 104-107 (scenes 3 and 4)
    Week 8: Video *Gene Blues.*

IV. Our Babies, Ourselves Infant rearing in different cultures. What can we learn about
  child care from other cultures?
    Week 9: Sleeping. What is SIDS? Where should infants sleep?
    Eating, Crying. What should infants eat? How often? Should we let them "cry it out?"

V. Research on Sex and Gender Caplan and Caplan
  What kinds of questions have scientists asked about sex and gender? How have the questions shaped their research? Would science change if there were more women scientists?
    Week 10: Chapters 1 & 2, pp. 1-30 How and why are scientists biased? Can we avoid
      such bias? What is Social Darwinism? What is sociobiology? What are some of the
      errors that may affect scientific research?
    Chapters 3-5, pp. 31-58. Define spatial abilities. Do men or women have better spa-
      tial abilities? Does the answer to this question matter? Why? Which sex is better in
      math? What is masochism? Are women masochistic?
    Week 11: Chapters 7-9, pp. 59-88 What is aggression? Is it good or bad? Which sex is
      more aggressive? How have scientists tested aggression? Is everything all Mom's
      fault?
    Bibliography due
    Chapters 10-12, pp.76-106 Do our hormones control us? Are they out of control?
      What is PMS?

VI. Environment. Was Rachel Carson the first ecologist? What is the significance of her work?
   Week 12: Carson Silent Spring. Video of Rachel Carson.

VII. Biographies. Who are the women scientists and what have they achieved? How did
   the scientific community treat them?
   Week 13: Mme Curie video Read biography of Marie Curie in Renaissance Women.
      Biography and scrapbook due.

VIII *Week 14:* Student Projects

THE UNIVERSITY OF ARIZONA

THE LABORATORY AND SOCIAL LIFE OF GENES

INSTRUCTORS:
Laura Briggs
lbriggs@u.arizona.edu

Sue DeNise
sdenise@ag.arizona.edu

OBJECTIVES:
- To explore the historical, social, and political life of genes as important mobilizers in contemporary culture.
- To learn the biological precepts governing the science of genes.
- To integrate understanding of this hybrid notion of a gene and how it affects public policy, human health, and everyday societal concerns.

READINGS:
The book for this course is Ruth Hubbard, *Exploding the Gene Myth*

SCHEDULE:
Week 1: Introduction, The history of the science of genetics
Week 2: Eugenics: Briggs; Reading: Chapters 1 & 2 from Hubbard
Week 3: The science of genes: DeNise; Reading: Chapters 4 & 5 from Hubbard
Week 4: The science of genes II: DeNise; Reading: Chapters 6 & 7 & afterword from Hubbard
Week 5: Laboratory Genetics: DeNise; DeNise will supply readings
Week 6: Public Policy and the Human Genome Project: Briggs; Reading: Chapter 8 Hubbard
Week 7: Genetic Screening—Reproductive Technology, School, Work: Briggs; Reading: Chapter 3 & 10, Hubbard
Week 8: Crime, DNA, and the OJ Trial: Briggs; Reading: Chapter 11, Hubbard
Week 9: Who Owns this Data? Corporate funding and Genetics: DeNise; Reading: Chapter 9, Hubbard
Week 10: Cloning: Defining the Positions; Reading: Conclusion, Hubbard
Week 11: Cloning: Research
Week 12: Cloning: What is possible?; Readings TBA
Week 13: Cloning: What is ethical?; Readings TBA
Week 14: Discussion: Presentation of Initial Positions
Week 15: Discussion: Dialogue
Week 16: Discussion: Conclusion

THE UNIVERSITY OF ARIZONA

CULTURES OF BIOLOGY, MEDICINE, GENDER, AND RACE

INSTRUCTORS:
Laura Briggs
lbriggs@u.arizona.edu

Meredith Trauner, Teaching Assistant
trauner@u.arizona.edu

FALL 2000

COURSE DESCRIPTION:
This course looks at the ways in which meanings of gender and race are influenced by popular conceptions of biology and medicine. It explores controversial topics such as gender difference in brain anatomy, genetic models of gayness and of intelligence, reproductive technology, hormones, and AIDS. Ideas about "scientifically" established differences among women and men, people of color and whites, and gays and straight are prevalent in popular culture. Using materials ranging from websites to blockbuster movies to magazines, we will explore the ways in which popular culture answers these questions and affects what we think and know about gender and race. For example, it surely matters to understand the struggles for racial equality over the past three centuries, in which most Europeans and Anglo-Americans believed that African Americans as a group are less intelligent than whites. Similarly, questions about women's fitness for certain jobs have often hinged on the belief that PMS makes women unreasonable and unable to make responsible decisions. We will explore the (thin) scientific justification for these beliefs, and the ways they are carried into popular culture.

Readings:
There are two texts for this course. Anne Fausto-Sterling, Myths of Gender (1992), designated "AFS" on the syllabus, and the course reader, available via the course web page (http://www.u.arizona.edu/ic/polis/fall00/Course-Homesite.cgi?W_S_210).

WEEK 1:
• What stories does popular science tell about sex and gender? Course overview
• Testosterone: Are You Man Enough?" *Time,* April 24, 2000; "The Science of Women and Sex," *Newsweek,* May 29, 2000
• Gender and Science: From Numbers to Knowledge to Cyborgs: *Ma Vie en Rose*

WEEK 2:
- AFS, ch. 1; Evelyn Fox Keller, "Introduction" *Reflections on Gender and Science*
- Helen Longino and Evelynn Hammonds, "Conflicts and Tensions in Feminist Studies of Science," in Marianne Hirsch and Evelyn Fox Keller, *Conflicts in Feminism*
- Anatomy and Physiology of Race and Gender—History; in-class presentations

WEEK 3:
- World Wide Web workshop
- Londa Schiebinger, "Why Mammals Are Called Mammals," *Nature's Body.*

WEEK 4:
- Stephen Jay Gould, "American Polygeny and Craniometry before Darwin: Blacks and Indians as Separate, Inferior Species," *The Mismeasure of Man.*
- "Gay Women's Inner Ear Works Like Men's, Researchers Find," *Toronto Star;* "Study Suggests Biological Basis for Lesbianism," *Washington Post;* "Finger Length Points to Sexual Orientation," *San Francisco Chronicle;* Anne Fausto-Sterling, "Of Gender and Genitals: The Use and Abuse of the Modern Intersexual" in *Sexing the Body.*
- Mothers and Reproduction; in-class presentations

WEEK 5:
- Ann Balsamo, "Public Pregnancies and Cultural Narratives of Surveillance," in *Technologies of the Gendered Body: Reading Cyborg Women*
- Ana Teresa Ortiz, "Bare-Handed Medicine and Its Elusive Patients: The Unstable Construction of Pregnant Women and Fetuses in Dominican Obstetrics Discourse," *Feminist Studies* 23:2.
- Molecules Make the (Wo)man: Genes for Gender, Race, and Sexual Orientation; in class presentations: *Genes and Gender*

WEEK 6:
- AFS, ch. 2 "A Question Genius: Are Men Really Smarter Than Women?"
- AFS, ch. 3 "Of Genes and Gender"
- in-class presentations: *Human Genome Project: Telling Stories of Race and Reproduction*

WEEK 7:
- Evelyn Fox Keller, "Master Molecules," in *Are Genes Us? The Social Consequences of the New Genetics;* Dorothy Nelkin and M. Susan Lindee, "Sacred DNA" in *The DNA Mystique: The Gene as Cultural Icon;* short film in class: Ellen DeGeneres and Sharon Stone, *If These Walls Could Talk*
- Diane Paul, "The Nine Lives of Discredited Data," *The Politics of Heredity;* Brent Staples, "The Scientific War on the Poor," (editorial) *New York Times* (October 28, 1994); Charles Murray and Richard Herrnstein, *New Republic* (October 31, 1994); J. Phillipe Rushton, "Genetics and Race," *Science* 271:5249.
- in-class presentations: Gay Genes

WEEK 8:
- AFS, ch. 8
- Dean Hamer, "Sex" in *Living with Our Genes: Why They Matter More than You Think.*
- in-class presentations: *Designer Babies, Clones, and Monsters*

WEEK 9:
- film, *Gattaca*
- Stephan Jay Gould, "Dolly's Fashion and Louis's Passion"; Andrea Dworkin, "Sasha," in Martha Nussbaum and Cass Sunstein, Clones and Clones; Thomas Kellner and Ben Pappas, "Rex Redux," *Forbes* 162:11.
- AFS, ch. 4 "Hormonal Hurricanes: Menstruation, Menopause, and Female Behavior"

WEEK 10:
- Nelly Oudshoorn, "The Measuring of Sex Hormones," *Beyond the Natural Body: An Archeology of Sex Hormones*
- AFS, ch. 5, "Hormones and Aggression"
- Animal Models; L. H. Studler, J.R. Reddon, K.G. Siminoski, "Serum Testosterone in Adult Sex Offenders: A Comparison Between Caucasians and North American Indians," *Journal of Clinical Psychology,* 53:4; A. Mazur, "Biosocial Models of Deviant Behavior Among Male Army Veterans," Biological Psychology, 41:3.

WEEK 11:
- Sarah Blaffer Hrdy, "Empathy, Polyandry, and the Myth of the Coy Female," in Ruth Bleier, ed. *Feminist Approaches to Science.*
- Sarah Blaffer Hrdy, "The Evolution of Female Orgasms: Logic Please but no Atavism," *Animal Behavior* 52; Randy Thornhill and Steven Gangestad, "Human Female Copulatory Orgasm: A Human Adaptation of phylogenetic holdover?" *Animal Behavior,* 52
- in-class presentations

WEEK 12:
- AFS, ch. 6 "Putting Woman in Her (Evolutionary) Place" Thornhill and Palmer, "Why do Men Rape?" *A Natural History of Rape* and Jerry Coyne and Andrew Berry, "Rape as Adaptation," *Nature* 404; Craig Stanford, "Darwinians Look at Rape, Sex, and War," *American Scientist* 88; Natalie Angier, "Biological Bull," Ms. (June/July).
- Paula Triechler, "Beyond Cosmo: AIDS, Identity, and Inscriptions of Gender," *Camera Obscura* 28
- Disease; in-class presentations: *Women, Teens, Race, and AIDS*

WEEK 13:
- Paula Triechler, "Beyond Cosmo: AIDS, Identity, and Inscriptions of Gender" *Camera Obscura* 28
- Cindy Patton, "Between Innocence and Safety," *Fatal Advice: How Safe Sex Education Went Wrong.*

WEEK 14:
- Rosalind Harrison-Chirumuuta and Richard Chirumuuta, "AIDS from Africa: A Case of Racism vs. Science?" *AIDS in Africa and the Caribbean.* J. Phillipe Rushton, "Population Differences in Susceptibility to AIDS: An Evolutionary Analysis," *Social Science and Medicine* 28:12.
- Randall Packard and Paul Epstein, "Medical Research on AIDS in Africa: A Historical Perspective," Elizabeth Fee and Daniel Fox, *AIDS: The Making of a Chronic Disease.*

WEEK 15:
- Richard Preston, "Crisis in the Hot Zone," *New Yorker* 68:36.
- Sandra Harding, "Is Science Multicultural? Challenges, Resources, Opportunities, Uncertainties," *Configurations* 2:2.
  Dec. 1—in-class presentations
- AFS, ch. 7 "Conclusion"

WEEK 16:
Review
Final exam

About AAC&U

AAC&U is the leading national association devoted to advancing and strengthening liberal learning for all students, regardless of academic specialization or intended career. Since its founding in 1915, AAC&U's membership has grown to more than 730 accredited public and private colleges and universities of every type and size.

AAC&U functions as a catalyst and facilitator, forging links among presidents, administrators, and faculty members who are engaged in institutional and curricular planning. Its mission is to reinforce the collective commitment to liberal education at both the national and local levels and to help individual institutions keep the quality of student learning at the core of their work as they evolve to meet new economic and social challenges.

AAC&U Statement on Liberal Learning

A truly liberal education is one that prepares us to live responsible, productive, and creative lives in a dramatically changing world. It is an education that fosters a well-grounded intellectual resilience, a disposition toward lifelong learning, and an acceptance of responsibility for the ethical consequences of our ideas and actions. Liberal education requires that we understand the foundations of knowledge and inquiry about nature, culture and society; that we master core skills of perception, analysis, and expression; that we cultivate a respect for truth; that we recognize the importance of historical and cultural context; and that we explore connections among formal learning, citizenship, and service to our communities.

We experience the benefits of liberal learning by pursuing intellectual work that is honest, challenging, and significant, and by preparing ourselves to use knowledge and power in responsible ways. Liberal learning is not confined to particular fields of study. What matters in liberal education is substantial content, rigorous methodology and an active engagement with the societal, ethical, and practical implications of our learning. The spirit and value of liberal learning are equally relevant to all forms of higher education and to all students.

Because liberal learning aims to free us from the constraints of ignorance, sectarianism, and myopia, it prizes curiosity and seeks to expand the boundaries of human knowledge. By its nature, therefore, liberal learning is global and pluralistic. It embraces the diversity of ideas and experiences that characterize the social, natural, and intellectual world. To acknowledge such diversity in all its forms is both an intellectual commitment and a social responsibility, for nothing less will equip us to understand our world and to pursue fruitful lives.

The ability to think, to learn, and to express oneself both rigorously and creatively, the capacity to understand ideas and issues in context, the commitment to live in society, and the yearning for truth are fundamental features of our humanity. In centering education upon these qualities, liberal learning is society's best investment in our shared future.

Adopted by the Board of Directors of the Association of American Colleges & Universities, October 1998. AAC&U encourages distribution, so long as attribution is given. Please address general inquiries to info@aacu.nw.dc.us